CHEMICAL BONDING

CHEMICAL BONDING

Audrey L. Companion

Department of Chemistry
Illinois Institute of Technology

McGRAW-HILL BOOK COMPANY

New York   San Francisco   Toronto   London

CHEMICAL BONDING

Library of Congress Catalog Card Number 64-22457

The *raison d'être* of this small volume is student interest, pro-voked during the past few years by lecturers in freshman chemistry at Illinois Institute of Technology. Some early supplementary notes on orbital theory distributed to the students were obviously well digested and stimulated many questions, criticisms, and arguments. These led gradually to the expansion of the notes to the present volume.

Most of the material included here has been used to supplement a one-year five-hour course in general chemistry, the first semester of which involves intensive drill in the *principles* of chemistry (structure, equilibrium, theory of solutions) and the second semester, a comprehensive survey of inorganic chemistry. Orbital theory is introduced early in the year and is used whenever possible to link together the many facts of inorganic chemistry.

The book may also be useful for supplementary reading in many advanced inorganic chemistry courses, introductory courses in valence theory, or In-Service courses for high school teachers.

The first two chapters, covering the experimental background and history of quantum theory, are purposely brief and may be omitted. Chapters 3 to 6 contain the basic rules governing the behavior of electrons in atoms, molecules, and solids, many applications of these rules, exercises for the student, and recommended further reading. Complete coverage of all important topics is not claimed, since the book is designed to supplement, not to replace, a good general chemistry or introductory inorganic textbook. More difficult sections are marked with asterisks in the Table of Contents and may be omitted without loss in continuity.

I am very grateful to the many students and staff members at IIT and friends at other universities for their suggestions and criticism. Additional suggestions for improvement are invited from readers. In particular, I wish to thank Dr. Kenneth Schug for his invaluable help in developing the final manuscript. Any errors remaining I claim as my own.

Audrey Companion

CONTENTS

chapter 4   Molecules and the Covalent Chemical Bond   37

chapter 5   Ionic, Metallic, and van der Waals Bonding   87

GLOSSARY OF SYMBOLS
AND ABBREVIATIONS

λ	wavelength of light
ν	frequency of light
$h\nu$	energy of a photon or quantum of light
I_1	first ionization energy
AO	atomic orbital
MO	molecular orbital
BMO	bonding molecular orbital
$ABMO$	antibonding molecular orbital
BO	bond order
μ	dipole moment
h	Planck's constant
R	Rydberg
Z	nuclear charge
P	promotional energy
$NBMO$	nonbonding molecular orbital
BM	Bohr magneton
EA	electron affinity
N	Avogadro's number
IP	ionic potential
A_M	Madelung constant
R_r	radius ratio
CN	coordination number
$CFSE$	crystal field stabilization energy
Δ	the octahedral splitting parameter

THE BEGINNINGS OF
QUANTUM THEORY

1

1-1 INTRODUCTION

Frustration and rebellion, though of a quiet sort, abounded in science in the early twentieth century, particularly among those concerned with the nature of matter and energy. Many new ideas were born, and many promptly buried; many old and established laws of physics were shaken. Out of this chaotic period emerged the modern theory of the structure of atoms, molecules, and solids, a theory virtually unchallenged today. A rigorous discussion of its basis requires at least a sound understanding of calculus, a tool usually not at the fingertips of initiates in chemistry. Yet even without the underlying mathematics we can describe quite well the nature of atoms and molecules, since the physical theory is rich in pictures and rules which are usually easily accepted. These we shall lean upon heavily in this text. Frequently though, we shall encounter concepts which seem unpalatable, for they defy the rules governing events occurring in everyday life. Yet accept them we must, for they are supported by unequivocal experimental evidence. One of these unusual concepts involves the dual life led by the phenomenon called light, with which we begin.

1-2 THE NATURE OF LIGHT

Largely because of the impact of the creative genius of Sir Isaac Newton (1642–1727), who advocated a corpuscular (particle-like) model, the wave theory of light propagation was not really accepted until about 1850, despite the accumulation of experimental evidence supporting it. At that time the experiments finally overwhelmed the particle model, and until the turn of the century the wave theory was undisputed. Many scientists felt that the corpuscular model had been properly and permanently put to rest.

Even now it is believed that light energy is *propagated through space* in the form of a wave motion, somewhat like ripples on a pond at the drop of a pebble. Figure 1-1 illustrates a representation of such a wave. The distance A is the maximum *amplitude* of the disturbance; the distance from crest to crest (or valley to valley) is its *wavelength* λ (Greek lambda), a distance quite large in a pond but very small when the wave motion describes light. For example, for visible light λ is only about 10^{-5} cm.

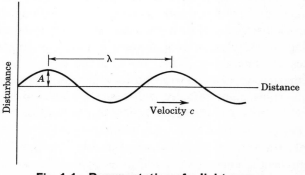

Fig. 1-1   Representation of a light wave.

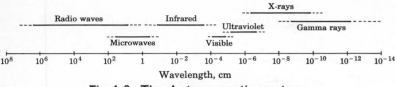

Fig. 1-2   The electromagnetic spectrum.

Light travels through space with a velocity c of approximately 3×10^{10} cm/sec; i.e., the peaks and valleys of Fig. 1-1 move in the direction of the light beam with a velocity c. In 1 sec a stationary microcosmic observer of a light beam of wavelength λ would count c/λ peaks passing by him, or would observe a frequency of peaks ν (Greek nu) of c/λ cycles per second associated with the wave.   Thus, *for light*, wavelength and frequency, both convenient descriptions of the wave property, are related by the equation

$$\lambda\nu = c$$

That which we call visible light is but a very narrow component of a large group of radiation types comprising the *electromagnetic spectrum* (Fig. 1-2), which includes very-long-wavelength radio waves and very-short-wavelength gamma rays.   All these radiation types are the same phenomenon; the basis for the classification shown in Fig. 1-2 is largely the experimental means of detection or generation.

The human eye is tuned to interpret only radiation of wavelength 4,000 to 7,000 Å (1 angstrom Å $= 10^{-8}$ cm), and these numbers are thus the limits of the visible portion of the electromagnetic spectrum.

There are many experimental "proofs" of the wave nature of light.   One, which will be of particular use to us later, involves the bending or diffraction of X-rays by orderly stacks of atoms in a crystal.   Figure 1-3 shows in cross section two X-rays of wavelength λ impinging at an angle θ on the surface of a crystal in which atoms are arrayed in planes separated by a distance d.   Both rays are associated with vibrations travel-

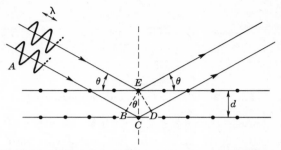

Fig. 1-3   Diffraction of X-rays by a crystal lattice.

ing in phase, so that their amplitudes maximize and minimize parallel to one another and they reinforce one another (point *A*), at least up to the line *BE*, after which the rays undergo reflections from different planes.   Now unless the distance *BCD* is equal to λ or to some integral multiple *n* of λ, the two emerging rays will be out of phase and may cancel one another. Through simple geometry *BCD* is $2d \sin \theta$, so that the condition for getting strong reflections from the crystal is

$$n\lambda = 2d \sin \theta \qquad \text{where } n = 0, 1, 2, 3, \ldots$$

the Bragg diffraction law.   Experimentally, if the angle of incidence of X-rays on a crystal surface is varied, strong reflections are observed at just the angles predicted, with blackness or grayness in between.   Such an experiment cannot be explained by a particle model of light.

However, in 1900 the German scientist Max Planck resuscitated corpuscular light while presenting a theory explaining blackbody radiation.   If the radiation emerging from a pinhole in a very hot closed furnace is passed through a prism and a graph of amount of energy emitted versus wavelength is constructed for a given temperature, a curve like one of those in Fig. 1-4 is obtained.   Explanations of these curves based on all the rules and regulations of physics known then (classical physics) failed to explain the shapes and temperature dependence of the curves.

Planck attacked this problem by searching for a formula connecting radiant energy, temperature, and wavelength, guessing different algebraic functions and adjusting them with numerical constants, until he found the correct *empirical* relationship between the variables. Armed with this, he then searched for a hypothetical "model" for the furnace system, from which he could derive theoretically his empirical formula. Success came rapidly when he compared the atoms constituting the walls of the furnace to a large assembly of oscillators of all vibrational frequencies, absorbing and emitting energy. One of the assumptions of his analysis was startling: the oscillators could change their energy by absorbing or emitting only spurts or bundles of energy which he called *quanta*. Furthermore, a quantum of energy was related to the oscillator frequency ν by the equation $E = h\nu$, where h is a proportionality constant, Planck's constant. When the absorption and emission probabilities of the group of oscillators were counted, a radiant energy distribution like that of Fig. 1-4 resulted. Such a distribution could not be obtained without these assumptions.

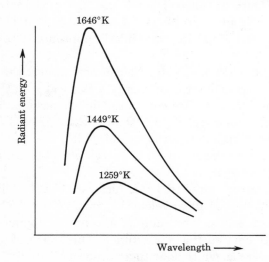

Fig. 1-4   Blackbody radiation.

Since until this time it was believed that a vibrating body could change its energy by any arbitrary amount (say 0.111 $h\nu$, 0.697 $h\nu$, etc.), quite possibly Planck's ideas would not have been accepted had it not been for Einstein's use of the quantum concept 5 years later in the explanation of the *photoelectric effect*. The experimental phenomenon here was the ejection of electrons from the surfaces of certain metals when bombarded with light.   Data connecting the intensity of light with the number of electrons freed and their velocities defied explanation in terms of the wave model.   Einstein explained all quite simply in terms of collisions between electrons of the metal and bundles of light (called photons) of energy $E = h\nu$.   A collision process is a corpuscular phenomenon!

Both models, corpuscular and wave, seem here to stay. Light, as it is propagated through space, is distinctly wavelike and, when it interacts with matter in energy-exchange processes, assumes a corpuscular nature.

We shall meet the unusual proportionality constant h again in the Bohr model of the atom (Chap. 2) and in the Schrödinger equation (Chap. 3), on which we base the modern theory of atoms and molecules and solids. h is now regarded as a fundamental constant of nature, particularly appropriate to systems of atomic size.

With the relation $E = h\nu$, we can now discuss the electromagnetic spectrum in terms of energy.   Since $\nu\lambda = c$, $E = hc/\lambda$, and since both h and c are constants, light energy is inversely proportional to its wavelength.   Radio waves are of low energy, gamma rays of high energy; near and within the visible range, infrared (IR) and red are of lower energy, violet and ultraviolet (UV) of higher energy.

The spectrum emitted by a furnace (Fig. 1-4) is a *continuum*, a display of all wavelengths, with no detectable gaps. Many heated solids, for example, a tungsten filament in an electric bulb, emit such a continuum.   This smear of all wavelengths appears as white light to an observer.

1-3 THE DUAL NATURE OF MATTER

The notion of the electron as a particle is commonly accepted
and has been for a long time now. Its wavelike character is
less well known.

Basing his arguments on the symmetry of nature, the
French physicist de Broglie postulated that, if light has both
particle- and wavelike character, a similar duality must exist
for matter, and he proceeded to show that a definite wavelength could be associated with the movement of bodies of
matter.

Previously Einstein had proved theoretically that mass
and energy were interconvertible quantities (a theory later
proved experimentally by nuclear physicists and chemists) and
had shown that associated with a photon of energy E was an
equivalent mass of E/c^2.   The momentum p (mass $\times$ velocity)
of a photon (a corpuscular property) is thus related to its wavelength (obviously a wave property) by

$$p = \text{mass} \times \text{velocity} = \frac{E}{c^2} c = \frac{h\nu}{c} = \frac{h}{\lambda}$$

i.e., momentum and wavelength are inversely proportional
through Planck's constant.

De Broglie postulated that with particles of matter of mass
m and velocity v was associated a wavelength λ given by

$$\lambda = \frac{h}{p} = \frac{h}{mv}$$

a relationship soon proved experimentally for electrons. A
pair of scientists, Davisson and Germer, tested the de Broglie
postulate by studying a beam of electrons accelerated to a high,
well-defined kinetic energy (and thus with well-known momentum and λ).   When directed at the surface of a nickel crystal,
the electron beam was reflected in much the same way as an

X-ray beam; construction and interference of the wavelike electron rays led to detectable electron scattering at angles predicted by an analysis like that of Bragg.

Thus physicists resigned themselves to the fact that electrons too have Jekyll-and-Hyde characters, sometimes behaving like particles and at other times like waves. In the ensuing chapters we shall use both portraits of the electron: a small compact negatively charged particle and a smeared-out wavelike negatively charged cloud. The reader is forewarned to accept both.

EXERCISES

1 Compute the energy in kilocalories per mole of radio waves of length 10^4 m and compare it with that of X-rays of length 1.54 Å. (Common units of energy and their interconversion factors are given in Appendix A.)

2 What are the limits of the visible spectrum expressed in electron volts?

3 Calculate the de Broglie wavelength of a 200-lb man moving with a velocity of 5 mph. If possible, classify this wavelength in the electromagnetic spectrum.

4 Calculate the wavelength of an electron beam accelerated to a kinetic energy $(\frac{1}{2}mv^2)$ of 100 ev.

5 Calculate the effective mass of an X-ray photon $(\lambda = 1.54$ Å) and compare with the mass of an electron, ca. 10^{-27} g.

REFERENCES

1 G. M. Barrow, "The Structure of Molecules: An Introduction to Molecular Spectroscopy," chap. 1, W. A. Benjamin, Inc., New York, 1963.

2 W. J. Moore, "Physical Chemistry," 3d ed., chap. 12, Prentice-Hall, Inc., Englewood Cliffs, N.J., 1962.

THE BOHR ATOM

2

2-1 INTRODUCTION

By 1913 the nature of the building blocks of the atom was well known.   In a series of experiments J. J. Thomson and R. A. Millikan had determined that the electron was a small, negatively charged particle of mass about 9×10^{-28} g and charge 4.8×10^{-10} esu.   By bombarding a thin gold foil with a beam of α particles, Rutherford had shown that most of the mass of the atom was concentrated in a small, positively charged body surrounded by largely empty space, and had postulated that the very small electrons were in some way located in this space, making the atomic unit neutral in charge.   Now obviously the electrons could not be standing still, for electrostatic attraction would quickly suck them into the nucleus.   Rutherford proposed that electrons were whirling at very high velocities in circular paths around the nucleus, so that the outward pull associated with such a motion would counteract the nuclear pull.   (Compare the outward pull on a bucket of water, counteracting gravitational pull, as it is swung in a vertical circle.)   Similar laws were known to govern the motion of planets around the sun, very successful laws.   Unfortunately for the theory, electrons differ from planets in that they are charged particles, and, according to other successful laws of classical physics, a moving charged particle will continually radiate (and lose) its energy.   The orbiting electron was thus doomed to lose its speed and quickly spiral into the nucleus. All attempts to build a model of the atom consistent with the experimental facts and with the laws of physics governing at that time led to disaster.   As Gamow (1) said, "it looked for a while as though either the physicists or physics itself had become completely insane."

It remained for the young physicist Niels Bohr to suggest a cure, but at the price of refuting some of the old and well-established laws of physics.   Bohr's revolutionary theory of the atom was prompted by his interest in certain experimental facts about the hydrogen atom, which we shall now examine.

2-2 OCCURRENCE OF LINE SPECTRA

In Chap. 1, the radiation emitted by a heated solid body was described as a continuous spectrum of all wavelengths and energies.   Figure 2-1 illustrates the *line spectra* obtained when one passes through a prism or grating the light emitted by strongly heated hydrogen atoms.   Not all energies of light are observed, but instead certain very discrete ones, which appear in the spectrum as sharp lines separated by blackness.   The energies of the lines are quite characteristic of the atom heated, and in fact the more prominent ones in the visible are the basis for the familiar flame tests used in qualitative analysis.   The

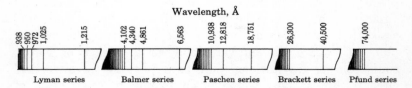

Fig. 2-1   Line spectra characteristic of the hydrogen atom.

line spectra in Fig. 2-1 belong to the hydrogen atom, and one can observe in the diagram several clusters or series of lines.

By a purely empirical approach J. J. Balmer found that the cluster of lines occurring in the visible and near ultraviolet had wavelengths which were interrelated by an equation easily reduced to the form:

$$\frac{1}{\lambda} = \mathbf{R}\left[\left(\frac{1}{2}\right)^2 - \left(\frac{1}{n}\right)^2\right]$$

where n is any integer greater than 2, and $\mathbf{R}$ is a constant, known as the Rydberg constant, whose value is 109,737 cm^{-1}. J. J. Rydberg and others showed that the wavelengths of all observed hydrogen clusters could be accounted for by the more general expression:

$$\frac{1}{\lambda} = \mathbf{R}\left[\left(\frac{1}{n_L}\right)^2 - \left(\frac{1}{n_H}\right)^2\right]$$

where n_H is an integer greater than the integer n_L. n_L takes on the following values for the different clusters: $n_L = 1$, Lyman series; $n_L = 2$, Balmer series; $n_L = 3$, Paschen series; $n_L = 4$, Brackett series; $n_L = 5$, Pfund series. Bohr intended to formulate a theoretical model for the hydrogen atom which would account for these rules.

2-3 STRUCTURE OF THE HYDROGEN ATOM

Bohr accepted Rutherford's notion of electron motion in circular orbits, but he rejected the classical law that moving charged bodies radiate energy and instead arbitrarily assumed (1) that the electron while in a particular orbit had a well-defined characteristic energy which *could not change* while it was in that orbit, and (2) that only *certain discrete energies were allowed* for the electron. By considering the influence of these assumptions on the balance of forces resulting from the circular motion and the electrostatic nuclear attraction, he was able to show that the energies available to the electron in hydrogen are given by

$$E_n = \frac{-2\pi^2 m e^4}{h^2 n^2}$$

Here e is the magnitude of the charge on the electron, m is the electron mass, h is the Planck's constant, and n is an integer, called the *principal quantum number*, which can take on the values 1, 2, 3, 4, . . . , each value of n defining a new energy for the electron. Associated with each energy is a circular orbit of well-defined radius around the nucleus given by

$$r_n = \frac{n^2 h^2}{4\pi^2 m e^2}$$

We can see that, as n approaches infinity, the nucleus and the electron are separated by an infinite distance, and consequently their attractive interaction energy must be zero. E_n in this limit is zero. As the orbits get closer to the nucleus (i.e., as n gets smaller), E_n becomes larger in *absolute value*, yet more and more negative. We shall identify the magnitude of E_n with the attractive energy holding the atom together (with its *stability*); yet because of its sign (which is determined by arbitrary convention), the most negative energy represents the most stable system with respect to the infinitely separated electron and nucleus. On an energy-level diagram such as Fig. 2-2, increasing energy (toward positive values) represents decreasing stability. Within this convention the state of lowest energy for the hydrogen atom is that for which $n = 1$. We name this the ground state of the system. All other allowed energies shown in Fig. 2-2 represent less stable, *excited* states. No energies between those indicated in Fig. 2-2 are permitted for the electron in the hydrogen atom.

Figure 2-3 shows the variation in orbit radii with n. When the electron is in its ground state ($n = 1$), it is in the orbit closest to the nucleus. According to Bohr theory it can go no closer.

The line spectra of the H atom can easily be interpreted in terms of the energy-level diagram given in Fig. 2-2, if it is assumed that the electron, excited to a higher, less-stable energy level E_H by a flame or spark, falls to a more-stable, lower state E_L, and in the process emits a photon or light quantum of energy $E_H - E_L$. Simultaneously it would move from a larger orbit with quantum number n_H to a smaller orbit characterized by n_L. Thus the photon energy would be

$$hv = E_H - E_L = \frac{2\pi^2 me^4}{h^2}\left[\left(\frac{1}{n_L}\right)^2 - \left(\frac{1}{n_H}\right)^2\right]$$

and accordingly we should have (since $v = c/\lambda$)

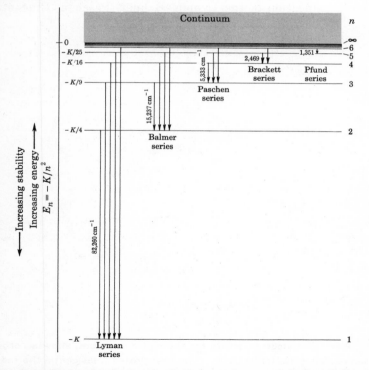

Fig. 2-2 Energy levels in the hydrogen atom and their relation to spectral series. $K = 2\pi^2 me^4/h^2$.

$$\frac{1}{\lambda} = \frac{2\pi^2me^4}{h^3c}\left[\left(\frac{1}{n_L}\right)^2 - \left(\frac{1}{n_H}\right)^2\right]$$

an equation compatible with the Rydberg equation provided that

$$\mathbf{R} = \frac{2\pi^2me^4}{ch^3}$$

R computed from separately determined values of these constants is in excellent agreement with the empirical value, and once Exercise 1 has been completed nothing more need be said about the validity of Bohr's model for the hydrogen atom. The identification of the Lyman, Balmer, Paschen, Brackett,

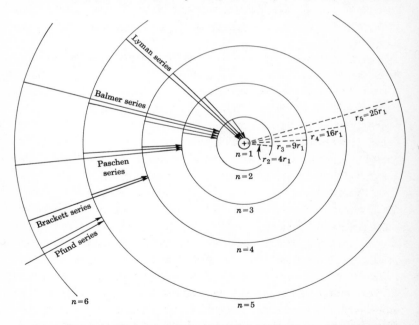

Fig. 2-3 Bohr electron orbits for the hydrogen atom, showing orbit changes for series transitions. The four dotted lines define the radii of the orbits in terms of the quantum number n and the smallest possible orbit r_1. $r_n = n^2r_1$ where $r_1 = h^2/4\pi^2me^2$.

and Pfund series in terms of the quantized energy levels provided by Bohr is illustrated in Fig. 2-2.

2-4 OTHER ATOMS

For other *one-electron systems*, such as the He^+ and Li^{++} ions, the Bohr model is equally good provided that we include the effect of the increased nuclear charge Z in the following way:

$$E_n = Z^2 E_n^H \qquad r_n = \frac{r_n^H}{Z}$$

where E_n^H and r_n^H are the expressions previously stated for the hydrogen atom.   For larger nuclear charges the stabilization energy of the electron is larger and the orbits are closer to the nucleus.

Although remarkably successful for these one-electron systems, Bohr theory when applied to many-electron (more than 1) atoms broke down almost completely, and it soon became apparent that more and more arbitrary postulates had to be introduced to bring the model into accord with experimental facts.   We shall not pursue these here, for soon (in about 10 years) the Bohr model was virtually abandoned in favor of the wave-mechanical theory in prominent use today.

Before closing the story of Bohr, we should pause to reflect on the impact of his work.   Though his assumptions of quantization were arbitrary and his results effective for only very simple systems, his courage in abandoning classical laws led (along with work of Einstein and Planck) to the now accepted philosophy that not all physical laws governing the macrocosm of ping-pong balls, people, and planets are applicable to the microcosm of electrons, photons, and particles of similar size. His place as one of the fathers of the old quantum theory is well deserved.   As we shall see, the new quantum theory negated none of his significant results, but rather confirmed the genius of his intuitive assumptions.

EXERCISES

1 Obtain from Appendix B accurate values of the fundamental constants e, m, c, and h and compute a theoretical value of the Rydberg constant. Compare this with the experimental value given in this chapter.

2 In terms of electron volts, the energy difference ΔE between a higher level with principal quantum number n_H and a lower level with quantum number n_L can be expressed as $\Delta E = 13.6Z^2[(1/n_L)^2 - (1/n_H)^2]$, where Z is the atomic number of a one-electron atom or ion.

(a) Calculate the energy which must be supplied to the H atom in order to remove its electron from its ground state to one where n_H is infinitely large, i.e., the energy necessary to remove the electron from the atom, its ionization energy I.

(b) Calculate the energy required to remove the electron from a Be^{3+} ion.

(c) Calculate the energy of the photon emitted when an electron on the Be^{3+} ion returns to its ground state from the $n = 2$ level.

REFERENCES

1 George Gamow, "One Two Three . . . Infinity," chap. VI, New American Library of World Literature, Inc., New York, 1954.
2 George Gamow, "The Atom and Its Nucleus," chap. 4, Prentice-Hall, Inc., Englewood Cliffs, N.J., 1961.
3 A. B. Garrett, The Flash of Genius, 9: The Bohr Atomic Model: Niels Bohr, *J. Chem. Educ.*, **39**, 534 (1962).

WAVE MECHANICS AND ATOMS

3

3-1 INTRODUCTION

More successful than the Bohr theory in explaining the structure and spectra of atoms is the mathematically sophisticated theory known as wave mechanics or quantum mechanics. Fortunately for us (the mathematically unsophisticated), one of the beauties of the theory is that it yields a treasure of simple rules and pictures from which we can gain an appreciation of the modern concepts of atomic structure.

3-2 THE SCHRÖDINGER EQUATION AND THE HYDROGEN ATOM

We begin by looking briefly at the equation formulated by Schrödinger in 1926, upon which almost everything we shall deduce about the behavior of the electron in the atom is based. For the simplest atomic system, the hydrogen atom, it is written

$$\frac{-h^2}{8\pi^2 m} \nabla^2 \psi + V\psi = E\psi$$

This weighty equation (which we need not understand in detail at this point) is simply a symbolical way of stating that the total energy of the hydrogen atom, E, is the sum of the potential energy (the term containing V) and its kinetic energy (disguised in the first term). Some of the symbols we have already met: h is Planck's constant, and m is the mass of the electron.

Since this equation was derived by Schrödinger from the classical equations governing the behavior of waves, it is known as the Schrödinger wave equation, hence the name "wave mechanics."

Like most algebraic equations, this one contains "unknowns" which must be solved for, denoted by the Greek letter ψ (psi, pronounced to rhyme with sigh); but unlike most algebraic equations, there are *many* ψ's which are acceptable solutions.† Finding them is not an easy task, but accommodating mathematicians have done this for us. Once found, the ψ's, which depend on the coordinates of the electron and are thus *functions* (wave functions), can tell us almost all that we want to know about the behavior of the electron in the hydrogen atom.

Let us pause to consider the "almost." Owing to what one might call the perversity of nature, the ψ's, though meaty with other information, cannot tell us the exact *position* of the electron in space at any specified time. Instead they tell us that the *probability* of finding the electron in some small chunk of space δv near the nucleus is related to $\psi^2 \, \delta v$. The larger ψ^2 is in some section of space, the more likely the electron is to be found there. The probability interpretation is consistent with the idea that the electron is a particle, though described by a *wave* function.

† The idea of an equation with many satisfactory solutions should not be new. For example, recall the simple trignometric equation

$$\sin \alpha = 0$$

for which $\alpha = 0, \pi, 2\pi, 3\pi, \ldots$ or, in general, $\alpha = n\pi$, where $n = 0, 1, 2, \ldots$, are all good solutions.

An interpretation perhaps more useful to chemists arises from the fact that in classical physics the intensity (photon density) of a light beam described by a wave function ϕ is related to ϕ^2. Hence we say that the magnitude of ψ^2 in some small element of space is a measure of the *electron density* there, even if we are dealing with a single-electron system. According to this interpretation, the electron is smeared out in space, its density being greatest in those places where the corpuscular electron is likely to be found. In a sense the electron may now be regarded as a diffuse cloud rather than a small discrete individual.

Since wave mechanics says that there is a finite (though very small) probability of finding the electron even a couple of miles away from the nucleus, these clouds have hazy rather than sharp boundaries. To distinguish these new pictures from the old well-defined Bohr *orbits*, we associate with these clouds the name *orbital*, or in short *AO* (for atomic orbital). Note that the *orbital* defines a most-probable volume in space where the electron may live; the orbital may be occupied or empty.

The size and shape of the *AO* depend on which of the wave functions ψ we are considering. As a consequence of solving the Schrödinger equation, each of the orbital ψ's has associated with it three characteristic interrelated quantum numbers called n, l, and m_l. These arise naturally from the Schrödinger equation in much the same way as the integer n results from the general solution of the simple trignometric equation mentioned in the preceding footnote, and they are by no means assumptions, as were the quantum numbers of Bohr.

The *principal quantum number* n determines the size of the orbital and also governs the allowed energy levels in the atom. n may assume the values 1, 2, 3, 4, . . . (any integer, not zero).

The quantum number l determines the shape of the orbital, and for any given value of n may assume the values 0, 1, 2, 3, . . . , $n - 1$, i.e., all integral values from zero up to a maximum of $n - 1$. For example, if $n = 4$, the l values associated with this n are 0, 1, 2, and 3.

The quantum number m_l has no effect on the size or shape of the orbitals but is related to the orientation of the orbital in space.   For our purposes, the allowed numerical values of the m_l will not be important, but instead what *will* be useful is the fact that for each l there are $2l + 1$ different possible values of m_l.   This means that there are $2l + 1$ different orientations or kinds of AO's with the same n and l.

The orbitals are named according to their values of n and l. The quantum number n appears in the name as an integer in front of the l value, where the latter is designated by the letter s, p, d, f, g, h, . . . according to whether l is 0, 1, 2, 3, 4, 5, ...

When l is zero, regardless of what n is, the orbital is called an s orbital.   There is only one kind of s orbital for any n, since for $l = 0$ the number of different possible m_l values ($2l + 1$) is 1. When l is 1, the orbital is called a p orbital.   Since here $2l + 1$ is 3, there are three kinds of p orbitals for a given n.   We shall name these p_x, p_y, and p_z, for reasons which will become obvious later.   When l is 2, the orbital is called a d orbital.   For this case, $2l + 1$ is 5, and there are five kinds of d orbitals for a given n.   These are named in Table 3-1, where some quantum numbers and orbital names of interest to us are summarized.

Table 3-1   Some Quantum Numbers and Corresponding Orbitals

n	l	Orbital names	$2l + 1$ Number of m_l values or number of kinds of each orbital	Full names of orbitals
1	0	$1s$	1	$1s$
2	0	$2s$	1	$2s$
	1	$2p$	3	$2p_x$, $2p_y$, $2p_z$
3	0	$3s$	1	$3s$
	1	$3p$	3	$3p_x$, $3p_y$, $3p_z$
	2	$3d$	5	$3d_{z^2}$, $3d_{x^2-y^2}$, $3d_{xy}$, $3d_{xz}$, $3d_{yz}$

The $spdf$ $\cdots$ names of the orbitals are intimately related to the shapes of the density clouds associated with them.   The hazy sphere of Fig. 3-1 represents an electron in a 1s orbital on the hydrogen atom. The nucleus of the atom is at the origin of the coordinate system.

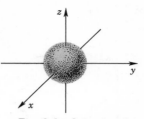

Fig. 3-1   A 1s **atomic orbital.**

Usually, instead of drawing the diffuse cloud or density pattern we represent orbitals by boundary surfaces (Fig. 3-2) containing most of (say perhaps 95 percent of) the electron density.   The probability of finding the electron within this boundary surface is then 0.95.   (Mathematicians define a probability of 1.00 to be equivalent to a certainty.)

The 2s orbital and indeed all s orbitals have spherical boundary surfaces.   However, as n gets larger, the bounding sphere gets larger (Fig. 3-2).

Within these spheres the electron density is not constant everywhere.   Figure 3-3 shows a plot of the electron density in some thin spherical shell at a distance r from the nucleus versus the distance r, for the 1s, the 2s, and the 2p orbitals.   Notice that for all of these the density is not constant and that for all the orbitals there is a radius of maximum electron density. . Somewhere within the boundary surface for a 1s orbital there will then be a single fuzzy spherical shell of high electron density and, within the 2s boundary surface, two concentric dense and fuzzy shells.

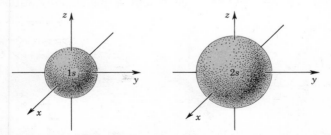

Fig. 3-2   Comparative boundary surfaces for 1s **and** 2s **orbitals.**

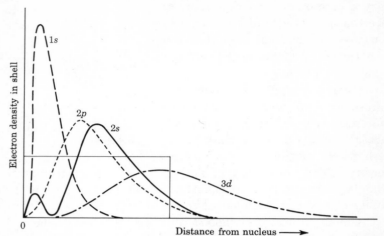

Fig. 3-3 Electron density distribution in $1s$, $2s$, $2p$, **and** $3d$ **orbitals as a function of distance from the nucleus. The straight lines represent the distribution expected if the electron cloud were of constant density, dropping abruptly to zero at the edge of the boundary diagram.**

All p orbitals (Fig. 3-4) have the same shape; their boundary surfaces resemble distorted dumbbells, and, in contrast to s orbitals, which are spherically symmetric, they possess directional properties. The p_x, p_y, and p_z orbitals are so called because their lobes of maximum electron density lie along the x, y, and z axes in space, respectively. An electron in a p_x orbital is somewhere in such a dumbbell-shaped space (95 percent of the time anyway), each lobe being equally probable.

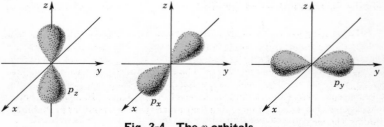

Fig. 3-4 The p **orbitals.**

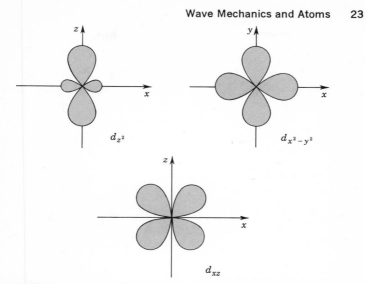

Fig. 3-5   Three of the five d orbitals in cross section.   These are shown in three dimensions in Fig. 6-5.

Note that both lobes constitute one p orbital and furthermore that the electron density within the lobes is not everywhere the same but maximizes and then tapers off as we proceed from the nucleus (Fig. 3-3).   The p orbitals, unlike s orbitals, have a plane of zero electron density, i.e., a so-called *nodal plane* separating the two lobes.†   For p_z, for example, the xy plane is the nodal plane.   Existence of these planes will be important in Chap. 4 when we try to classify different types of bonds.

Three of the five d orbitals are shown in Fig. 3-5. d_{z^2} has a shape somewhat different from the other four; most of its density is concentrated around the z axis, the largest part of

† Often students are troubled by the seemingly paradoxical statement that an electron in a p orbital occupies each lobe with equal probability, although the lobes are separated by a nodal plane.   The question arises: How does the electron get from one lobe to another?   The answer we prefer is that the plane has mathematical not physical significance; i.e., it has zero thickness.   It makes no sense to speak of finding a particle in that plane.   In a slice of finite thickness on either side of or including that plane there is a nonzero probability of finding the electron.

the volume being somewhat p-orbital-shaped but with a dough-nut-shaped cloud encircling its middle. The other four d orbitals all have a clover-leaf shape with four lobes each (two nodal planes). The $d_{x^2-y^2}$ orbital lies in the xy plane with its four lobes coinciding with the x and y axes; d_{xy} also lies in the xy plane, but with its lobes pointed between the axes; d_{xz} and d_{yz} lie in the xz and yz planes, respectively, and like d_{xy} have their lobes of electron density pointed between the axes.

The shapes of s, p, and d orbitals are particularly important in chemistry, whereas those of f, g, and higher orbitals are not. Hence we have not attempted to draw the latter.

With respect to energy, wave mechanics says that the electron in the hydrogen atom is governed by the same relationship that Bohr derived:

$$E_n = \frac{-2\pi^2 e^4 m}{n^2 h^2}$$

The lowest-energy state (the most stable state) of the electron in the hydrogen atom is that for which $n = 1$, corresponding to occupation of the $1s$ orbital. Higher-energy states (excited states) are those for which n is greater than 1. The spacings of these higher-energy states relative to the lowest (ground) state are shown on the ordinate of Fig. 3-7. For the hydrogen atom, the energy of the orbitals depends only upon the principal quantum number n (and not on l or m_l), and consequently the $2s$ and the three $2p$ AO's all have the same energy. The $n = 2$ level is said to have a fourfold orbital *degeneracy*; four different AO's belong to this same energy level. Similarly the $n = 3$ level is ninefold degenerate, since the $3s$ orbital, the three $3p$ orbitals, and the five $3d$ orbitals all have exactly the same energy.

Wave mechanics, like Bohr theory, says that the *emission spectrum* of the hydrogen atom results when electrons are excited to levels of higher n and subsequently fall back down to lower states, each downward jump being accompanied by the emission of a quantum of light, a photon.   Here though, the electron is changing its *orbital* rather than its *orbit.*

3-3 MANY-ELECTRON ATOMS

The Schrödinger equation has been solved exactly only for one-electron systems, primarily because, even in a simple atom like helium $(Z = 2)$, the repulsion between the two electrons makes the potential energy term V tremendously complicated.   Thus the orbitals, quantum numbers, and pictures that we have discussed are not rigorously true even for He.   However, there are many experimental facts which indicate that in larger atoms something quite like the quantum numbers n, l, and m_l governs the behavior of the electrons.   This in turn implies that states like the s, p, d, f, . . . atomic orbitals exist and are occupied by these many electrons; consequently, we extrapolate the one-electron orbital results to bigger atoms.   Justification for doing this is that it works!

Before we discuss the extrapolation (called *Aufbau,* or build-up), we state the existence of a fourth quantum number for the electron, namely, m_s, its "spin" quantum number. Unlike n, l, and m_l, m_s did not evolve from the Schrödinger equation but was invented by experimentalists shortly before the Schrödinger equation was postulated.   Uhlenbeck and Goudsmit found that a great deal of spectroscopic data could be explained if it were postulated that the electron is able to spin in one of two possible directions about an arbitrary axis through its center (Fig. 3-6).   According to the direction of spin we assign to the electron $m_s = +\frac{1}{2}$ or $-\frac{1}{2}$. Usually we refer to these as α or β spin, and in comparing

Fig. 3-6   Electron spin around an arbitrary z axis.

two different electrons use the notation ⇈ to mean same or unpaired spins (either $\alpha\alpha$ or $\beta\beta$) and ⇅ to mean spins opposite or paired ($\alpha\beta$).

The existence of spin causes us to add to our collection of rules the *Pauli exclusion principle*, which states that each orbital can be a home for at most two electrons, and then only if their spins are opposite or paired ($\alpha\beta$). For example, consider the hydride ion H^- (present in compounds of certain metals with hydrogen, such as LiH). Starting with the *neutral* hydrogen atom:

H $(Z = 1)$: $1s^1$

(meaning that the charge on the nucleus Z is $+1$ and that there is one electron in the $1s$ orbital), we add one electron more to the $1s$ AO to make

H^- $(Z = 1)$: $1s^2$

or pictorially to show the electron pairing H^-: ⇅ $1s$

No more electrons can be accommodated in the $1s$ orbital.

The helium atom is isoelectronic (having the same number of electrons) with the hydride ion but has two protons in the nucleus. Because of this increased nuclear charge we should expect the two electrons in He to be more tightly bound to the atom than those in H^-. It would require more energy to remove an electron from the vicinity of the nucleus, or in other words the $1s$ orbital of He would be more stable than that of H. The ground-state configuration of He would still be

He $(Z = 2)$: $1s^2$ or pictorially   He: ⇅ $1s$

For the lithium atom with three electrons, after pairing two electrons in the $1s$ orbital, we are faced with the problem of where the third electron lives. If the orbital energy levels in the Li atom were the same as those in H, it would not matter whether this last electron were assigned to the $2s$ or to a $2p$ orbital, since for H all of these possess the same energy.

Let us reexamine Fig. 3-3. Note that, even though the most probable location of a 2p electron is closer to the nucleus than that of a 2s electron, the electron density close to the nucleus is greater for a 2s than for a 2p orbital. Because of this we say that a 2s electron "penetrates" closer to the nucleus than a 2p electron. In the lithium atom an electron in a 2s AO penetrates the electron cloud of the 1s electrons and sees more of the positive charge on the nucleus than an electron in a less penetrating 2p AO, which sees a nuclear charge shielded by the two 1s electrons. Hence the 2s electron is more strongly attracted, is more difficult to ionize, and is in a stabler state (lower in energy) than an electron in a 2p orbital.

Because of this penetration and shielding effect, part but not all of the orbital energy degeneracy evident in the hydrogen atom is removed. The three 2p orbitals all have the same penetrating power and consequently the same energy in a many-electron atom.

In general, for any given principal quantum number n, s AO's are lower in energy than p AO's, which are lower than d AO's, etc., since the penetrating powers vary as follows:

Most penetrating $= s > p > d > f > g > h \cdots$

Figure 3-7, constructed from theoretical and experimental considerations, shows how the orbital energies may change in neutral atoms as the size of the atom increases. Note that, as the atom gets larger, in certain cases the principal quantum number loses control of the energy, and the orbital-energy lines cross; for example, 4s becomes lower than 3d because of the high penetrating power of the s orbital even though, according to the principal quantum number, 3d should be lower in energy. We shall discuss this crossover in detail in Sec. 3-4.

For many of the lighter elements a rough qualitative rule of orbital energies is:

Lowest $= 1s < 2s < 2p < 3s < 3p < 4s < 3d < 4p < 5s < 4d \cdots$

$n + l = 1 \quad 2 \quad 3 \quad 3 \quad 4 \quad 4 \quad 5 \quad 5 \quad 5 \quad 6$

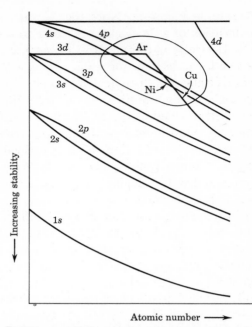

Fig. 3-7 Relative orbital energies for neutral atoms. The circled section is enlarged in Fig. 3-8.

The $n + l$ values are listed as a mental crutch.   Usually the energy varies first as $n + l$, and within a group of identical $n + l$ the orbital with highest l is lowest in energy.

If we return now to the *Aufbau* principle and the question of Li, its ground-state configuration is obviously

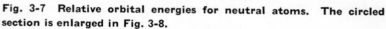

Li $(Z = 3)$: $1s^2\ 2s^1$

and those of others across the periodic table:

Be $(Z = 4)$: $1s^2\ 2s^2$

B $(Z = 5)$: $1s^2\ 2s^2\ 2p^1$

C $(Z = 6)$: $1s^2\ 2s^2\ 2p^2$

For carbon we introduce *Hund's rule*, which in essence says that electrons prefer to occupy separate orbitals with their spins unpaired (the same) provided that it is energetically reasonable. Since all three of the $2p$ orbitals have the same energy, the two $2p$ electrons in carbon are quite happy to occupy separate homes, say arbitrarily $2p_x$ and $2p_y$. To pair in the same orbital requires a considerable expenditure of energy by the electron, since the first one occupying an orbital looks rather repulsive to the second.

Why then do not the two electrons in helium enter one into the $1s$ orbital and the other into the $2s$ orbital? In a sense, the second electron must decide which is greater: the energy lost by occupying the less stable $2s$ orbital or the energy lost in overcoming the repulsion of the $1s$ electron. Since the energy separation between the $1s$ and $2s$ levels is relatively large (see Fig. 3-7), the lesser of these two evils is the latter.

Continuing across the periodic table (Appendix C), we have

			$1s$	$2s$	$2p$		
N	$(Z = 7)$:	$1s^2\, 2s^2\, 2p^3$	⬆	⬆	⬆	⬆	⬆
O	$(Z = 8)$:	$1s^2\, 2s^2\, 2p^4$	⬆⬇	⬆⬇	⬆⬇	⬆	⬆
F	$(Z = 9)$:	$1s^2\, 2s^2\, 2p^5$	⬆⬇	⬆⬇	⬆⬇	⬆⬇	⬆
Ne	$(Z = 10)$:	$1s^2\, 2s^2\, 2p^6$	⬆⬇	⬆⬇	⬆⬇	⬆⬇	⬆⬇

Between the $2p$ and the $3s$ levels there is a considerable energy gap (Fig. 3-7). In fact, for low Z there are at least four groups of levels characterized by being close to one another in energy and separated by a wider gap from other groups. These are $1s$ (a group in itself); $2s$, $2p$; $3s$, $3p$; and $4s$, $3d$, $4p$. Each group makes up what may be called an energy shell, similar to Bohr's shells around the atom. Filling one of these shells with its quota of electrons corresponds to attaining the peculiar stability associated with the rare gases. The first four rare gases, their energy shells, and the capacities of these (in parentheses) are:

	(2)	(8)	(8)	(18)
He $(Z = 2)$:	$1s^2$			
Ne $(Z = 10)$:	$1s^2$	$2s^2\ 2p^6$		
Ar $(Z = 18)$:	$1s^2$	$2s^2\ 2p^6$	$3s^2\ 3p^6$	
Kr $(Z = 36)$:	$1s^2$	$2s^2\ 2p^6$	$3s^2\ 3p^6$	$3d^{10}\ 4s^2\ 4p^6$

Orbital theory thus makes it reasonable that the period from neon to argon should comprise only 8 members and that the period from potassium to krypton should include 18 elements.

By means of the orbital theory the entire periodic table is given a sound theoretical basis. For example, all the members of one family (vertical column) have similar external electronic configurations; these are responsible for the similarity in chemical behavior of most members of the family. In the two following illustrations the similar external parts are in bold-faced type.

The Alkali Metals (*Group* I)

Li $(Z = 3)$:	(He core)^2 **2s^1**
Na $(Z = 11)$:	(Ne core)^{10} **3s^1**
K $(Z = 19)$:	(Ar core)^{18} **4s^1**
Rb $(Z = 37)$:	(Kr core)^{36} **5s^1**

All the alkali metals readily lose one electron (the outermost s electron) to form singly positive ions Li^+, Na^+, K^+, Rb^+ with rare-gas configurations, but it is extremely difficult to ionize them further to doubly positive species.

The Halogens (*Group* VII)

F $(Z = 9)$:	(He core)^2 **2s^2 2p^5**
Cl $(Z = 17)$:	(Ne core)^{10} **3s^2 3p^5**
Br $(Z = 35)$:	(Ar core)^{18} $3d^{10}$ **4s^2 4p^5**

The halogens readily *gain* one electron (completing their outer-most p levels) to form singly negative ions F⁻, Cl⁻, Br⁻. These have the structure of the next highest rare gas, Ne, Ar, and Kr, respectively. Doubly negative halide ions are not known; once the rare-gas configuration is attained, there is little or no tendency to gain more electrons.

The lengths of the fourth and fifth periods (10 extra members as compared to the second and third periods) are caused by the large number of electrons (10) necessary to fill up the $3d$ and $4d$ levels, respectively.

The 24 "extra" members of the sixth period result from the filling of the $4f$ and $5d$ levels (14 and 10 electrons, respectively).

3-4   ATOMS AND IONS OF THE FIRST TRANSITION SERIES

Application of the *Aufbau* principle to atoms from helium ($Z = 2$) to argon ($Z = 18$) is rather straightforward; there are no exceptions to the general rules outlined in the previous section. After potassium [(Ar core)¹⁸ $4s^1$] and calcium [(Ar core)¹⁸ $4s^2$], the $3d$ level gradually fills up as we progress across the first transition series from scandium [(Ar core)¹⁸ $4s^2$ $3d^1$] to zinc [(Ar core)¹⁸ $4s^2$ $3d^{10}$] with but two apparent exceptions at chromium [(Ar core)¹⁸ $4s^1$ $3d^5$] and copper [(Ar core)¹⁸ $4s^1$ $3d^{10}$], both of which have an incomplete $4s$ level. The latter two cases may be understood if we examine in Fig. 3-8 a blowup of the crossover area circled in Fig. 3-7.

In region A, covering elements from H to Ar, the ground-state configuration of the atom includes no $3d$ or $4s$ electrons; thus the lines in Fig. 3-8 represent energies of electrons excited from the core to the $4s$ or $3d$ levels. Now consider what an excited electron sees at the core as we go from H to Ar. Simultaneously we increase the nuclear charge and add electrons to the core. A $4s$ electron, being very penetrating, sees this increased charge and becomes more tightly bound, and the $4s$ level drops in energy. A $3d$ electron, only weakly penetrating, sees little change in the nuclear charge as the core grows larger; its energy or stability remains relatively constant.

After argon we arrive in region B, where $4s$ electrons are added externally as the nuclear charge increases. The $4s$ electrons have a high density in the same region of space as the $3d$ electron. Thus, being no longer between the $3d$ electron and the nucleus, the added $4s$ electrons do not shield the $3d$ electron from the increased nuclear charge, and the $3d$ level now begins to drop in energy owing to increased nuclear attraction. The drop becomes so fast as electrons are added to the d level that $3d$ eventually becomes lower in energy than $4s$, the crossover point defining region C. Experimentally it seems that the crossover occurs just after the nickel atom [(Ar core)^{18} $4s^2$ $3d^8$], so that for the next atom, Cu, $3d$ is considerably lower in energy than $4s$, and the 11 electrons outside the Ar core take the configuration $3d^{10}$ $4s^1$.

The apparent exception Cr ($4s^1$ $3d^5$) still remains, for, in region B, $4s$ is still lower than $3d$. For Cr, however, the $3d$ and $4s$ levels are close enough that Hund's rule prevails, and the spin stabilization obtained by allowing the six electrons to occupy singly the $4s$ and five $3d$ orbitals offsets the energy necessary to promote the electron from what would seem to be the more stable $4s^2$ $3d^4$ configuration. The ground-state configurations of all atoms from argon to zinc are shown in Table 3-2.

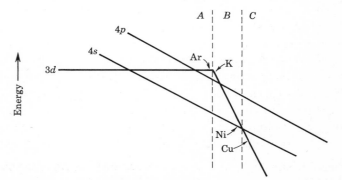

Fig. 3-8 Orbital energies for atoms near the first transition series.

Table 3-2   Ground-state Configurations of Transition-metal Atoms and Ions

Ar	$(Z = 18)$:	$1s^2\ 2s^2\ 2p^6\ 3s^2\ 3p^6$		
K	$(Z = 19)$:	(Ar core)^{18} $4s^1$	K$^+$:	(Ar core)^{18}
Ca	$(Z = 20)$:	(Ar core)^{18} $4s^2$	Ca^{++}:	(Ar core)^{18}
Sc	$(Z = 21)$:	(Ar core)^{18} $4s^2\ 3d^1$	Sc^{++}:	(Ar core)^{18} $3d^1$
Ti	$(Z = 22)$:	(Ar core)^{18} $4s^2\ 3d^2$	Ti^{++}:	(Ar core)^{18} $3d^2$
V	$(Z = 23)$:	(Ar core)^{18} $4s^2\ 3d^3$	V^{++}:	(Ar core)^{18} $3d^3$
Cr	$(Z = 24)$:	(Ar core)^{18} $4s^1\ 3d^5$	Cr^{++}:	(Ar core)^{18} $3d^4$
Mn	$(Z = 25)$:	(Ar core)^{18} $4s^2\ 3d^5$	Mn^{++}:	(Ar core)^{18} $3d^5$
Fe	$(Z = 26)$:	(Ar core)^{18} $4s^2\ 3d^6$	Fe^{++}:	(Ar core)^{18} $3d^6$
Co	$(Z = 27)$:	(Ar core)^{18} $4s^2\ 3d^7$	Co^{++}:	(Ar core)^{18} $3d^7$
Ni	$(Z = 28)$:	(Ar core)^{18} $4s^2\ 3d^8$	Ni^{++}:	(Ar core)^{18} $3d^8$
Cu	$(Z = 29)$:	(Ar core)^{18} $3d^{10}\ 4s^1$	Cu^{++}:	(Ar core)^{18} $3d^9$
Zn	$(Z = 30)$:	(Ar core)^{18} $3d^{10}\ 4s^2$	Zn^{++}:	(Ar core)^{18} $3d^{10}$

For the *ions* of these elements no discontinuities occur in the filling of the d level.   Normally the atoms lose at least two electrons in the ionization process, and the configurations of the ions reflect a gradual filling of the d orbitals (Table 3-2).   It seems puzzling that for all these ions the $4s$ rather than $3d$ electrons are gone, particularly since for most of the neutral atoms the $4s$ electrons are lower in energy, more stable than the $3d$. The experimental facts, however, are unequivocal and indicate that in the ions the $3d$ level must drop much earlier than it does in the neutral atoms.   It seems quite probable that even in neutral atoms shielding of nuclear charge by core electrons is not a one-to-one process and that in the metal ions complete loss of two shielding electrons is sufficient to allow the d electron to see the increasing nuclear charge and drop in energy sooner. Effects like this and the so-called anomalous behavior of neutral chromium and copper are results of highly complex interelectronic forces and cannot as yet be predicted accurately.   We can only (as in much of chemistry) search the experimental facts and try to propose reasons for the observed behavior.

EXERCISES

1 Which of the following orbitals do and which don't "make sense" according to wave mechanics?   Explain your answers.

> $2d$ $6h$ $7g$ $3f$

2 What is the maximum number of electrons that can be accommodated in

> all the $6g$ orbitals?
> all the $7s$ orbitals?
> all the $8f$ orbitals?
> all the orbitals with $n = 5$?

3 Write the complete ground-state electronic configurations of the first three members of the nitrogen family: N $(Z = 7)$, P $(Z = 15)$, and As $(Z = 33)$, showing all unpaired electrons. Underline the parts responsible for their similarity in chemical behavior.

4 Without referring to the text write ground-state electronic configurations for the following atoms, applying Hund's rule whenever appropriate:

> Mg $(Z = 12)$ Mo $(Z = 42)$
> Si $(Z = 14)$ Xe $(Z = 54)$
> Ca $(Z = 20)$ I $(Z = 53)$
> Ni $(Z = 28)$ Cs $(Z = 55)$

5 List all ions of the first or second transition series with d^5 or d^{10} ground-state configurations.

6 In general, the first ionization energies (energies required to remove one electron from the neutral atom) increase as we go across the second period (see below).   Why?   However, boron and oxygen exhibit anomalous behavior; their ionization energies are lower than expected.   Examine the electronic configuration of these elements and suggest why.

	Li	Be	B	C	N	O	F	Ne
$I_1(\text{ev}) =$	5.4	9.3	8.3	11.3	14.5	13.6	17.6	21.6

7 The energy required to remove the outermost electron from the Sr atom is 5.69 ev; removal of a second electron requires almost twice as much energy, 10.98 ev.   In comparison, although the first ionization energy of Rb is 4.18 ev, removal of a second electron requires almost seven times as much energy, 27.36 ev.   Suggest a reason for these facts on the basis of orbital electronic configurations.

8 Beginning with $4d$, predict the next five orbitals in increasing energy for a many-electron atom; i.e., continue the series given as an illustration of the $n + l$ rule in Sec. 3-3.   What would a similar ordering of all these levels be in the hydrogen atom?

REFERENCES

Frequently a student's inability to grasp a difficult concept is due not to his innate impenetrability but rather to a particular author's lack of "penetrating power."   The cure obviously is to find an author whose presentation is more effective.   For this purpose we append a list of suggestions for further reading of important concepts introduced in this chapter.   None of these references will read like a novel.   They are all advanced works.   However, early in the game it is useful to learn to scan difficult treatises in search of a clarifying paragraph, sentence, word, or picture—and then pounce on it!   It is a rare scientific work which is completely comprehensible to the average reader on its first reading.

1 R. B. Heslop and P. L. Robinson, "Inorganic Chemistry," Elsevier Publishing Company, Amsterdam, 1960.

2 E. Cartmell and G. W. A. Fowles, "Valency and Molecular Structure," Butterworth & Co. (Publishers), Ltd., London, 1956.

3 C. Coulson, "Valence," Oxford University Press, Fair Lawn, N.J., 1952.

4 D. de Vault, The Electronic Structure of the Atom, *J. Chem. Educ.*, **21**, 526, 575 (1944).

5 J. A. Campbell, Atomic Size and the Periodic Table, *J. Chem. Educ.*, **23**, 525 (1946).

6 D. F. Swinehart, The Building-up Principle and Atomic and Ionic Structure, *J. Chem. Educ.*, **27**, 622 (1950).

7 L. E. Miller, A Periodic Chart Based on *spdf* Electron Distribution, *J. Chem. Educ.*, **32**, 199 (1955).

8 R. H. Maybury, The Language of Quantum Mechanics, *J. Chem. Educ.*, **39**, 367 (1962).

9 R. N. Keller, Energy Level Diagrams and Extranuclear Building of the Elements, *J. Chem. Educ.*, **39**, 289 (1962).

MOLECULES AND THE
COVALENT CHEMICAL BOND

4

4-1 INTRODUCTION: MOLECULAR ORBITAL FORMATION

To define a molecule, we may say that it is a discrete group of atoms held together by a chemical bond. This in turn requires definition of a chemical bond, and this we shall try to supply in this chapter.

Just as the hydrogen atom is the simplest atom, the hydrogen molecule, H_2, is the simplest kind of molecule. What happens when a bond between two hydrogen atoms forms? To answer, let us watch two isolated H atoms, each with its electron in its ground-state $1s$ orbital, approach one another (Fig. 4-1).

Atoms, like humans, are continually seeking a state of greater security or stability, and we may imagine that these two atoms in their approach are looking one another over, counting the pros and cons of merger. As they get closer and closer, the $1s$ clouds containing the electrons begin to overlap. Each electron feels attracted to the approaching nucleus, and overlap increases. The two atomic orbitals merge into one

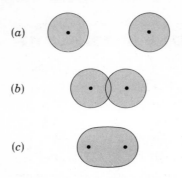

(a)

(b)

(c)

Fig. 4-1 **Molecular orbital formation from** s **orbitals.** (a) **Two isolated atomic orbitals;** (b) **overlap;**
(c) **the molecular orbital boundary
diagram.**

bigger cloud called a molecular orbital (MO), and in it the electrons find that they are strongly attracted to both nuclei.
When the repulsive forces between the positively charged
nuclei have determined the position of closest approach, the
merger halts.   At this point the system of two nuclei and two
electrons has attained a stability surprisingly greater than that
of the two isolated atoms, and the molecule is born.

Figure 4-2 shows graphically the energy changes just described.   At large values of the internuclear distance R, the
energy of the system is just that of two isolated hydrogen
atoms.   Arbitrarily we call this energy zero, so that any more

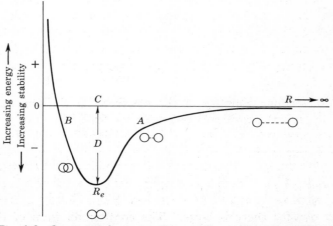

Fig. 4-2 **A potential-energy diagram for a diatomic molecule.**

stable state of the system will be described by a negative energy. As R decreases, the stability increases, largely because of the dual nuclear attractive forces acting on the electrons. At some point R_e (the equilibrium internuclear distance) the stability maximizes (as the energy minimizes), since, past this distance, at smaller R, the strong repulsion between the nuclei causes the curve to rise steeply.

An energy curve like this is sometimes called a potential well, because the behavior of the system it describes parallels the behavior of a rubber ball in a curved "well" of the same shape. If such a ball were placed at point A in Fig. 4-2, it would roll down to the bottom and eventually stop at the point designated by R_e. Similarly, if one supplies enough energy to the molecule to stretch it (increasing its R and its energy to position A), the *point* describing the physical state of the system, the analogue of the ball, will "roll back down into the well" when the stretching forces are released. Similar arguments hold for compression of atoms in a molecule (situation B in Fig. 4-2).

An energy D would be required to lift the rubber ball out of the well. Similarly, an energy D is sufficient to lift the molecule at its equilibrium distance out of the well. Above the well at C the energy of the system is just that of two isolated atoms; there is no bonding energy and the atoms may fly apart. Thus the energy D closely approximates the experimental *dissociation energy* of the molecule into its component atoms in their ground states.

The peculiar stability of the electrons in the molecular orbital in H_2 is the fundamental reason for bond formation. In the molecular orbital (MO), the two electrons are shared equally between the nuclei and are no longer identifiable with either of the nuclei. This sharing corresponds to what chemists call a *covalent bond*. Logically enough, the two shared electrons are now more likely to be found between the two nuclei, and the electron density there is large. The contour diagram of the MO is thus somewhat contracted parallel to the internuclear axis and expanded at the center of the molecule. As shown in Fig. 4-1, the MO contour diagram is *not* simply a superposition of the AO contours.

This particular kind of molecular orbital is called a σ (Greek sigma) MO, and more explicitly may be designated σ_{1s}, since it was formed by merger of two $1s$ AO's. The subscripts are usually necessary, since, as we shall see in the next section, sigma-type MO's may be formed by appropriate merger of any type of AO ($2s$, $2p$, $3d$, $4f$, . . .). For hydrogen we may write the ground-state configuration of the *molecule* as

H_2: σ_{1s}^2

Even in MO's the electrons are haunted by the Pauli exclusion principle, and consequently the two electrons in the ground-state MO of H_2 must have their spins paired.

Just as in the atom, there are available in the molecule many higher-energy, less-stable MO's, which may be constructed by merging $2s$ AO's, $2p$ AO's, etc. These will be discussed in detail in Sec. 4-11.

4-2 GENERAL PROPERTIES OF MOLECULAR ORBITALS

There are only three kinds of MO's that we need worry about in chemistry: the σ (sigma) MO's, usually associated with strong bonds, and their progressively weaker relatives, π (pi) MO's and δ (delta) MO's. To illustrate the differences between them, we consider construction of σ and π MO's from $2p$ orbitals.

In Chap. 3 we learned that p orbitals may be represented by dumbbell-shaped clouds lying along one of the x, y, or z axes, each p orbital having two lobes separated by a plane of zero electron density, a nodal plane. For the p_z orbital the nodal plane is simply the xy plane. It is important at this point to remember that the labeling of particular axes, x, y, or z, is completely arbitrary; we may label them and relabel them to suit

our purpose.   The electron in an orbital knows nothing of the
letters x, y, or z.

Consider now two p_z orbitals on different atoms overlapping head on, by pointing directly at one another, as shown in
Fig. 4-3.   The boundary diagram of the MO formed by the
merger indicates that the electron density has piled up between
the nuclei, and as a consequence the density in the outer lobes
has decreased.   Note that the MO thus formed has two nodal
planes perpendicular to the internuclear axis, but *no nodal plane
containing the internuclear axis.*   This latter characteristic is
the criterion for distinguishing a σ MO from all other MO types.
Note that the σ MO formed from 1s orbitals had no such nodal
plane.

When the MO is occupied by two electrons, we say that
the atoms are joined by a σ bond.   Sigma bonds are the strong-
est kind of covalent bond, with the largest bond dissociation
energies.

In contrast, two p_z orbitals on different atoms could approach one another sideways, as shown in Fig. 4-4.   The boundary diagram after merger again shows increased electron density
between the nuclei, and moreover the molecular orbital formed
has a nodal plane *containing* the internuclear axis (the xy plane).
Such a molecular orbital is called a π MO.   All π MO's have
one and only one nodal plane containing the internuclear axis.

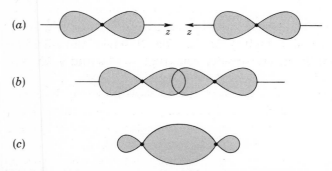

(a)

(b)

(c)

Fig. 4-3   Sigma molecular orbital formation from p orbitals.   (a) **Two
isolated** p_z AO's; (b) **head-on overlap;** (c) **the** σMO **boundary diagram.**

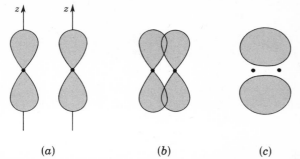

Fig. 4-4   Pi molecular orbital formation from p **orbitals.** (a) **Isolated** p_z AO's; (b) **sideways overlap;** (c) **the** πMO **boundary diagram.**

Both the sausage-shaped lobes are part of the same π MO, just as the two lobes of an isolated p_z AO together constitute the orbital. When the π MO is filled with two electrons, the result is a π bond between the two atoms. Pi bonds are generally weaker than σ bonds.

Figure 4-5 shows the formation of a δ MO from two $3d$ orbitals overlapping face to face. The four sausagelike clouds all belong to the same MO. Superficially the δ MO resembles two perpendicular π MO's; however, two π MO's could accommodate four electrons, while the δ MO, even with four lobes, can accommodate only two electrons. Note the existence of *two*

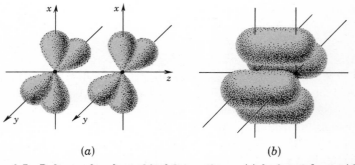

Fig. 4-5   Delta molecular orbital formation. (a) **Isolated** $d_{x^2-y^2}$ AO's; (b) **the** δMO.

nodal planes containing the internuclear axis (the xz and the yz planes).

From the discussion thus far we can conclude that σ, π, and δ *MO*'s have 0, 1, and 2 nodal planes, respectively. The reader should satisfy himself that (1) *only* σ *MO*'s can be constructed from s *AO*'s, (2) *only* σ and π *MO*'s can be constructed from p *AO*'s, and (3) σ, π, and δ *MO*'s can be constructed from d *AO*'s.

4-3 APPLICATION TO THE NITROGEN MOLECULE

A molecule considerably larger than H_2, yet similar in that it is homonuclear (same nuclei), is the nitrogen molecule N_2. As the first step in the analysis of its *MO* structure, we consider the ground-state electronic configuration of the nitrogen atom, applying Hund's rule:

N $(Z = 7)$: $1s^2\ 2s^2\ 2p_x^1\ 2p_y^1\ 2p_z^1$

In the simplest approach we can assume that, since the $1s$ and $2s$ orbitals on the nitrogen atoms are already filled with paired electrons, they will not contribute much to bonding and will not enter into *MO* formation. In this approximation we are treating them as "nonbonding" or "core" electrons, assuming that they will remain largely near their respective nuclei, forming "cores" like [N $(Z = 7)$: $1s^2\ 2s^2$], around which the *MO*'s will form by merger of the $2p$ orbitals. If we orient the coordinate systems of two nitrogen atoms a and b so that the two $2p_y$ *AO*'s are pointed at one another (Fig. 4-6a), then a σ *MO* will result from their overlap, accommodating the two $2p_y$ electrons (Fig. 4-6b). Upon sideways overlap of the $2p_x$ *AO*'s and the $2p_z$ *AO*'s, two π *MO*'s (four sausage-shaped clouds) will form, surrounding the σ *MO*, as shown in Fig. 4-6c. Each of these π *MO*'s will hold two electrons, so that the six electrons originally in $2p$ *AO*'s in the isolated atoms are now located two in a σ *MO* and two each in the π *MO*'s. This combination of

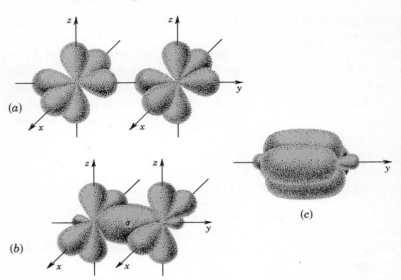

Fig. 4-6 Molecular orbitals in the nitrogen molecule. (a) **The three half-filled** p **orbitals on each N atom;** (b) **overlap along the** y **axis to form a** σMO; (c) **the "sausage" clouds of two** πMO's **formed by overlap along the** x **and** z **axes.**

one σ bond and two π bonds corresponds to a triple bond between the atoms, so that in the classical line structure of N_2, $N\equiv N$, one line represents a σ bond and the other two π bonds.

The electronic configuration of the N_2 molecule may be written

$$N_2: \quad 1s_a^2\ 1s_b^2\ 2s_a^2\ 2s_b^2\ \sigma_y^2\ \pi_x^2\ \pi_z^2$$

where we have abbreviated σ_{2p_y} as simply σ_y, since there is no ambiguity in doing so.

To be rigorous, we must recall that the boundary surfaces that we have been drawing are by no means *barriers* to the electrons; there is a finite probability that a π_x electron may wander into a $\pi_z MO$ region and even into the σMO region. As a result of this the π cloud surrounding the σMO will not necessarily exhibit the well-defined bumps shown in Fig. 4-6c. Experimentally the nitrogen molecule is known to be cylindrically symmetrical; i.e., a microcosmic observer sitting near the arrow on the y axis looking at the molecule would see a circularly shaped cloud. All cross sections perpendicular to the internuclear axis would be circular. Thus the superposition of two π MO's formed from mutually perpendicular sets of p AO's must yield a smooth π cloud encircling the axis, even though the nodal planes of the π MO's, considered as individuals, are still present. Note also that the presence of the σ MO cloud along the internuclear axis does not interfere with the definition of the respective π MO's. Each has its nodal plane. In classifying the MO's we must consider each separately, as though it were there alone.

4-4 SOME SIMPLE HETERONUCLEAR MOLECULES

Diatomic molecules whose nuclei are not alike (heteronuclear) can be treated by similar pairing schemes. Consider the molecule HF. The ground state of the F atom is

F $(Z = 9)$: $1s^2\ 2s^2\ 2p_x^2\ 2p_y^2\ 2p_z^1$

The half-empty $2p_z$ AO, when aimed at the $1s$ AO of a hydrogen atom, could overlap to form a σ MO with a shape somewhat like that in Fig. 4-7, containing the H $1s$ electron and

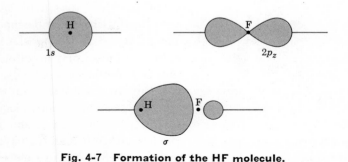

Fig. 4-7 Formation of the HF molecule.

the F $2p_z$ electron with spins paired to form a σ bond. (Note the *perpendicular* nodal plane.) All the other fluorine electrons may be considered *nonbonding.* Those pairs that are more external in location are called *lone pairs* and, as we shall see later, have a large influence on the shapes of molecules. The lone pairs in HF are the $2p_x$ and the $2p_y$ electrons. The $1s$ and $2s$ electrons are considered *core* electrons.

The configuration of HF may be written

$$\text{HF:} \qquad 1s_\text{F}^2 \, 2s_\text{F}^2 \, 2p_{x\text{F}}^2 \, 2p_{y\text{F}}^2 \, \sigma^2$$

Suppose that we consider a larger molecule: H_2O, water. The electronic structure of the oxygen atom is

$$\text{O } (Z = 8)\text{: } 1s^2 \, 2s^2 \, 2p_x^1 \, 2p_y^1 \, 2p_z^2$$

We shall regard the $1s$ and $2s$ electrons as core electrons. In Fig. 4-8 these are not shown, and for simplicity only one lobe of each p orbital is drawn. The $2p_z$ orbital (shaded) is already filled with a lone pair of electrons and is thus not available for bonding. If two hydrogen atoms with proper spin approached the p_x and p_y orbitals head on, two σ bonds, each with a shape like that in HF, would form. Accordingly we should expect the water molecule to be nonlinear with a bond angle, determined by the nuclear positions, of about 90°, since this is the angle between the p_x and p_y orbitals. The experimental H—O—H angle is 105°, in reasonably good agreement with this simple model. The mutual repulsion of the two hydrogen nuclei may account for the 15° difference.

We can extrapolate immediately to the ammonia molecule, NH_3. The nitrogen atom has one less electron than the oxygen atom, and thus has one electron

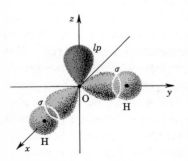

Fig. 4-8 The p^2 model of the water molecule.

each in the $2p_x$, $2p_y$, and $2p_z$ orbitals. As shown in Fig. 4-9, three σ bonds may form when three hydrogen atoms approach these p orbitals head on. Thus in the ammonia molecule the four atoms would not lie all in the same plane, but rather form a pyramid whose base is the three hydrogen atoms, with the N atom at the apex of the pyramid. The experimental H—N—H bond angles are 106°, somewhat larger than the pre-

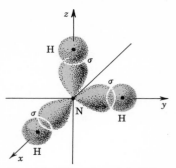

Fig. 4-9   The p^3 model of the ammonia molecule.

dicted 90°, but the general three-dimensional shape of the molecule certainly agrees with that predicted by this simple model.

In a later section, when the concept of hybridization has been introduced, we shall discuss improved models for ammonia and water molecules, models predicting bond angles in better agreement with experiment.

4-5 BOND POLARITY AND ELECTRIC DIPOLE MOMENTS

For homonuclear molecules like H_2, N_2, and O_2, there is no question about whether the electron pair in the bonding MO is shared equally by the two nuclei. Since both atoms making up the molecule are the same, both pull equally on the bonding electrons. But for heteronuclear atoms this is not true. Certain atoms of the periodic table are particularly electron-greedy (have a high *electronegativity*) and, when involved in a bond, tend to take more than their share of the bonding electron pair. The most electron-greedy atom is fluorine; following that are O, N, and Cl. Roughly, electronegativity decreases across the periodic table from *right to left* and down the table within a family. As the difference in electron greediness of two atoms in a heteronuclear bond increases, the MO cloud of the bonding pair is distorted toward the more electronegative atom, and the character of the bond departs more and more from pure covalency.   In the extreme case of little or no sharing, we have an *ionic bond*, i.e., a system of a positive and a negative ion held together by electrostatic forces.   This case will be discussed in detail in the next chapter.

Between these extremes, equal sharing and no sharing, we can describe bonds as being partially covalent or partially ionic, and a particularly useful vehicle for quantitatively describing these systems is the measurable molecular property called the electric dipole moment.

We can best illustrate what the dipole moment is by first considering a molecule without one, H_2.   In an isolated hydrogen atom the singly negative electron in its ground state is spread about in a sphere surrounding the singly positive nucleus.   The center of positive charge is the center of the nucleus and similarly the center of negative charge (the average position of the electron) is the center of the nucleus.   (Note that this is true whether the orbital describing the electron is *s*-, *p*-, or *d*-shaped.)   Thus the centers of positive and negative charge *on the atom* coincide.

As two H atoms approach one another, the center of positive charge for the system is at the center of their internuclear distance, coincident with the center of negative charge, since the electron pair is equally shared.   Such a molecule has no dipole moment.

For a *he'eronuclear* molecule like HF, the isolated atoms still have coincident centers of negative and positive charge. As they approach, the center of positive charge is somewhere between them, closer to the heavier atom, and until the bonding pair overlaps, the center of negative charge is at the same point.   If, however, when overlap occurs, the electron-greedy atom pulls the bond pair toward it, the center of negative charge will move with the pull and will no longer coincide with the positive-charge center.   Molecules whose positive- and negative-charge centers do not coincide are said to possess an *electric dipole moment,* frequently represented by a little arrow or vector with tail sitting at the positive center and head pointing at the negative center.   The length of the arrow represents the magnitude of the dipole moment.

Quantitatively this dipole moment is measured in terms of a unit called a Debye (D), defined such that a positive and a negative charge (each equivalent to the electron charge) separated by a distance of 1 Å has a dipole moment of 4.8 D.   Generally the dipole moment μ is given by

$$\mu = zr_0$$

where z is the magnitude of the charges separated by the distance r_0.

The electric dipole moment of a molecule may be measured by placing the substance between the plates of a capacitor.   In the presence of the electric field between the capacitor plates the little dipoles tend to line up (so far as their molecular motion, determined by the temperature, permits) with their positive ends pointing at the negative capacitor plate and their negative ends toward the positive plate; this orientation results in a decrease in the electric field strength between the plates and an increase in the *capacitance* of the capacitor.   The capacitances of the capacitor plates when separated by a vacuum, C_0, and when separated by a substance S, C_S, are related by a factor called the *dielectric constant* ϵ of S:

$$C_S = \epsilon C_0$$

Measurement of these capacitances and consequently the dielectric constant allows one to calculate the magnitude of the dipole moment.   More details are given in (4) and (16).

Pauling (3) has suggested that these measured dipole moments may be used to estimate the percentage of ionic character of a bond.   Consider the molecule HF; its measured internuclear distance is 0.9171.   If it were completely ionic, i.e., if it consisted of neighboring H^+ and F^- ions with no sharing,

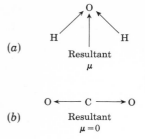

(a)

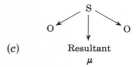

(b)

(c)

Fig. 4-10 Addition of dipole-moment vectors for (a) H_2O; (b) CO_2; (c) SO_2.

its dipole moment would be 4.4 D (0.9171 times 4.8). Its measured dipole moment is 1.91 D, so that it is not 100 percent ionic, but only 1.91/4.4 times 100 percent, or 43 percent ionic. Note that according to this definition the molecules HCl, HBr, and HI have decreasing ionic and therefore increasing covalent character.†

In the water molecule (Fig. 4-10a) each bond has its own dipole moment because of the electron greediness of the oxygen atom, and these moments added vectorially yield a resultant dipole moment for the molecule, represented by the vector bisecting the H—O—H bond angle.

That the CO_2 molecule has a zero μ, even though C and O have different electronegativities, indicates that somehow the arrows representing the C—O bond dipole moments cancel. This can be true only if they are equal and pointed in opposite directions (Fig. 4-10b). Thus CO_2 must be a linear molecule with the carbon atom in the center.

Obviously SO_2 (Fig. 4-10c), with a dipole moment of 1.61 D (Table 4-1), must be bent like H_2O, so that the bond moments do not cancel.

† Note that this definition of ionic character implies that a completely covalent bond (0 percent ionic character) would have *no* dipole moment. This is not strictly true for a heteronuclear molecule, since, owing to the difference in shape or size of two overlapping orbitals (1s and $2p_z$ in HF), the bond pair may experience a distortion while shifting from AO's to an MO, and this distortion may be sufficient to destroy the coincidence of charge centers, even though the bond pair is equally shared. Coulson (15) describes in detail this and other contributions to the dipole moment, all of which make the picture considerably more complicated than the simple model described here. Nevertheless, the Pauling definition is quite useful for making qualitative predictions.

That the μ's for BCl_3 and CH_4 are zero (Table 4-1) means that the geometry of these molecules must be such that the resultant magnitude of the bond dipole vectors must be zero.

Table 4-1   Electric Dipole Moments of Some Common Molecules

Molecule	Internuclear distance, Å	μ, D	Molecule	μ, D
HF	0.9171	1.91	H_2O	1.85
HCl	1.275	1.03	NH_3	1.49
HBr	1.413	0.78	CO_2	0.0
HI	1.604	0.38	SO_2	1.61
			BCl_3	0.0
			CH_4	0.0

1 Debye $= 1$ D $= 10^{-10}$ esu-Å

We shall use this information later when we discuss the bonding in these molecules.

4-6   NEED FOR THE CONCEPT OF HYBRIDIZATION

We return now to a survey of the *MO* structures of simple molecules and consider $BeCl_2$, a molecule experimentally known to be linear in shape with a chlorine atom on either side of the Be atom.   Now an isolated Be atom has a ground-state electronic configuration $1s^2\ 2s^2$, and hence at first glance we might expect Be to behave chemically like the inert gas He, which has its $1s$ orbital filled and shows no tendency to form molecules with other atoms.   However, if we refer to Fig. 3-7, we see that for Be there is another energy level lying quite close to the outermost filled level.   For He this is not true.   Orbitals on the same atom which lie close to one another in energy have an unusual ability to combine with one another in an additive way, forming what are called *hybrid* orbitals.   The phenomenon of hybridization is best illustrated with some pictures.

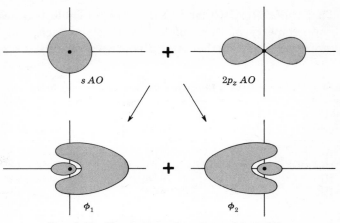

Fig. 4-11   Formation of sp digonal hybrids.

An s orbital can combine with a p orbital *on the same atom* to form two new and completely equivalent orbitals in the manner shown in Fig. 4-11. Note that the resulting unsymmetrical hybrid orbitals (named ϕ_1 and ϕ_2) have properties of both the s and p orbitals which were smeared together to form them. The hybrids are "fatter" than pure p orbitals but have the directional characteristics of p orbitals. Those particular hybrids are called digonal or sp hybrids, since one s orbital and one p orbital were sacrificed to make them. Figure 4-12 illustrates a common abbreviation of hybrid shape.

If we assume that in the $BeCl_2$ molecule the Be atom has

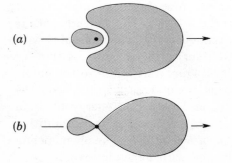

Fig. 4-12   The actual shape of a hybrid (a) and its abbreviation (b).

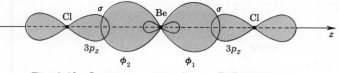

Fig. 4-13   Structure of the linear BeCl₂ molecule.

its two outer electrons arranged one each in two sp hybrids (instead of both in the $2s$), then the molecule may be pictured as shown in Fig. 4-13, where two chlorine atoms have lined themselves up so that the two hybrids on Be are pointed directly at their half-filled $3p_z$ AO's.   Overlap creates two σ MO's, each with two electrons.   The filled $1s$, $2s$, $2p$, $3s$, $3p_x$, and $3p_y$ AO's on each Cl atom are not shown.   The MO structure is consistent with the molecule's linear geometry.

At this point, and as we proceed through other examples, the skeptic may rebel at the concept of hybrid formation, proclaiming that it is only an artificial device enabling us to rationalize bonding in systems for which use of pure orbitals fails to give us any reasonable picture.   Then he must recall that, after all, the Schrödinger equation has been solved exactly only for the hydrogen atom and that only for this one species are the s, p, d, f, . . . orbitals rigorous descriptions of electron behavior.   We have no right to be upset because *all* molecules cannot be described by electron pairing among pure H-like AO's.   Hybrids and MO's are approximations to the "true" but unattainable solutions to the Schrödinger equation for molecules.

We may introduce two more common types of hybridization by examining some common carbon-containing molecules, for example, methane gas, CH₄.   Experiment tells us that the four bonds in this molecule are equivalent; but when we examine the electronic structure of the isolated carbon atom, $1s^2\, 2s^2\, 2p_x{}^1\, 2p_y{}^1$, we see that there appear to be only two electrons available for pairing and bond formation, namely, the two unpaired p electrons.   Since the $2s$ orbital is quite near the $2p$ in energy (see again Fig. 3-7), we may first promote one

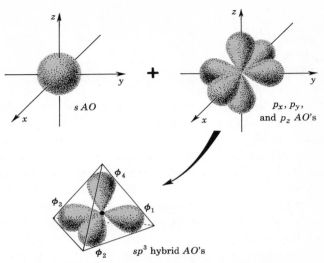

Fig. 4-14   Formation of tetrahedral sp^3 hybrids.

of the $2s$ electrons to the $2p$ level, thus obtaining the "excited" configuration $1s^2\, 2s^1\, 2p_x{}^1\, 2p_y{}^1\, 2p_z{}^1$, which because of its four unpaired electrons is at least associable with four bonds.   Three of the bonds, however, would be different from the fourth (that formed from the $2s$ orbital), and experiment says that this is not true.

An answer is again found in the phenomenon of hybridization.   The $2s$ and the three $2p$ orbitals may combine or smear together (all four of them this time) to give four new and equivalent hybrid orbitals called sp^3 or tetrahedral hybrids.   This process is pictured in Fig. 4-14.   The four resulting hybrids all have shapes similar to the sp hybrids of Fig. 4-12, but here they are directed in space toward the corners of a regular tetrahedron, the carbon nucleus (and the $1s$ electron core) being at the center of the solid figure.   In Fig. 4-14 the smaller lobes of the hybrids are not shown.   If each of these hybrid AO's contains one of the four unpaired electrons of the excited carbon atom, we may suppose that bonding occurs when the four hydrogen atoms, each with one unpaired $1s$ electron, approach the four apexes of the tetrahedron and overlap with the hybrid AO's.   Four equivalent σ bonds form.   The shape of the CH_4 molecule would consequently be like that of a tetrahedron; experimentally this is true.   Furthermore, as stated in Sec. 4-5, the overall electric dipole moment of CH_4 is zero, a fact consistent with its highly symmetrical shape.   The resultant of the four vectors representing bond dipole moments is zero.   (A student familiar with vector analysis may easily prove this. See Exercise 14.)

Now let us look at the somewhat more complex molecule ethane, C_2H_6.   A line formula showing how the atoms are connected is given in Fig. 4-15a.   The molecule, however, is not planar as the figure implies, but rather has the shape indicated in Fig. 4-15b.   The two carbon atoms are located at the centers of two tetrahedra, and two apexes of the tetrahedra meet on the line connecting the carbon nuclei.   The six hydrogen atoms are arranged at the other six apexes of the tetrahedra, and, in order that the repulsion between the hydrogen nuclei may be minimized, the tetrahedra are twisted so that the apexes are separated by 60° (Fig. 4-15c).   With this experimental knowl-

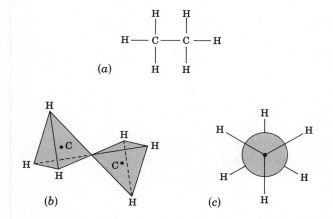

Fig. 4-15   Structure of the ethane molecule, C_2H_6.   (a) Line formula; (b) tetrahedral CH_3 groups connected by a σ bond; (c) side view showing the relative orientation of the two CH_3 groups.

edge, it is easy to explain what the bonding electrons are doing. Each carbon atom is in an sp^3 state of hybridization; a σ bond is formed between the carbons by overlap of two hybrid AO's along the carbon-carbon internuclear axis; the six hydrogen atoms are bonded in σ fashion with the remaining six tetrahedral hybrids. It is known experimentally that the two CH_3 groups may rotate with respect to one another about the σ bond connecting them. A relatively small amount of energy is necessary to overcome the repulsion of bond pairs and hydrogen nuclei between the two groups.

Plunging ahead to a similar molecule, ethylene, C_2H_4, we first examine the experimental facts. The atoms of ethylene, unlike those of ethane, all lie in the same plane, i.e., are coplanar. The total strength of the bond(s) connecting the two carbon atoms is considerably greater than that in ethane (almost, but not quite, twice as much), and, furthermore, the two CH_2 groups *cannot* rotate with respect to one another. These latter two facts indicate the existence of more than just a σ bond between the carbon atoms; i.e., some π formation is

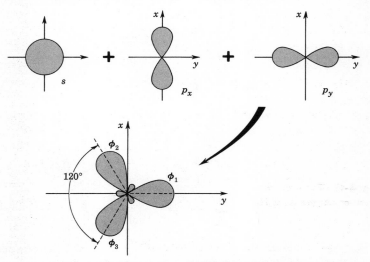

Fig. 4-16 Formation of sp^2 trigonal hybrids.

likely.   (The student should satisfy himself that two molecular
fragments connected by just a σ bond may rotate with respect
to one another *without breaking the bond*, but that two fragments
connected by a σ and a π bond are restricted in rotation unless
the π bond is broken.)

In order to rationalize the structure of this molecule, let us
again consider the promoted configuration of the carbon atom,
$1s^2 \, 2s^1 \, 2p_x{}^1 \, 2p_y{}^1 \, 2p_z{}^1$.   This time, instead of forming sp^3 hybrids,
we shall leave one of the p electrons (arbitrarily the $2p_z$) in its
pure orbital, and mix or hybridize the $2s$ with the $2p_x$ and the
$2p_y$ orbitals.   Mixing these three will give us three equivalent
hybrid orbitals, all lying in the xy plane, since we have mixed
into the hybrids only the x- and y-preferring p orbitals.   The
shapes and orientation of the hybrids, called trigonal or sp^2
hybrids, are illustrated in Fig. 4-16.

After forming two sets of these trigonal hybrids, one set on
each carbon atom, we shall line up the two carbons so that all
the hybrids are lying in the same plane and so that one on each
carbon atom overlaps to form a carbon-carbon σ bond (Fig.
4-17).   The other two hybrids on each carbon form σ bonds
with hydrogen atoms.   The resulting planar structure is called
the σ *framework* of the molecule; it lies in the xy plane.

The one electron on each carbon atom which we left in a
pure p_z unhybridized state will occupy an orbital perpendicular
to the plane of the σ framework (Fig. 4-18a).   Overlap of these
two p_z AO's sideways gives rise to a π MO, illustrated in Fig.
4-18b.   Since the energy of a π bond is less than that of a σ

**Fig. 4-17 The σ frame-
work of ethylene, C_2H_4.**

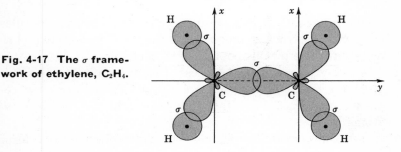

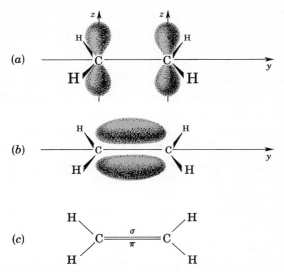

Fig. 4-18 Pi molecular orbital formation in ethylene. (*a*) **The** p_z **orbitals before overlap;** (*b*) **the** π **cloud after overlap;** (*c*) **the line formula indicating** σ **and** π **bonds.**

bond, the amount of energy necessary to rip ethylene into two CH_2 fragments is less than twice the energy for fragmentizing ethane into two CH_3 groups.

The classical line formula for ethylene is given in Fig. 4-18*c*, where the double line means one σ plus one π bond.

4-7 A SUMMARY OF HYBRIDIZATION RULES

Before discussing more molecules we pause to collect the rules of hybrid construction presented in the previous section and to point out some pitfalls popular with beginners.

1. Hybridization is a process of mixing orbitals *on a single* atom (or ion). In contrast, molecular orbital formation requires smearing of orbitals originally centered on *different* atoms.

2. Only orbitals of similar energies can be mixed to form

good hybrids.   For our purpose this will mean that the orbitals usually must belong to the same "energy group" as shown in Fig. 3-7.

3. Always, the number of orbitals mixed together equals the number of hybrids obtained.

4. In hybridization we mix a certain number of *orbitals*, not a number of electrons.   For example, if we wish to form digonal (sp) hybrids on an atom in a three-electron configuration $2s^2\ 2p^1$, we mix the s and p orbitals to get two hybrids ϕ_1 and ϕ_2, and then arrange the electrons among them, possibly as $\phi_1^2\phi_2^1$.

5. Once an orbital has been used to build a hybrid it is no longer available to hold electrons in its "pure" form.   For example, in item 4 above, a configuration $2s^1\ \phi_1^1\ \phi_2^1$ is illegal, for the $2s$ orbital no longer exists as such.

6. Most hybrids are similar, but they are not necessarily identical in shape; they differ from one another largely in orientation in space.   A proper representation of the sp hybrid is shown in cross section in Fig. 4-12.   The three-dimensional shape is cut out of space by rotating the z axis without translating it in space, i.e., rolling it between the fingers.

7. Since s orbitals have no dominant direction in xyz space, they add no direction when contributing to hybrids.   They add "plumpness" only.

8. Other orbitals with pronounced directions in space (p_x, p_z, d_{xy}, d_{yz}, etc.) determine the directional properties of hybrids. Mixing only x-liking and y-liking orbitals with s orbitals gives hybrids preferring the xy plane; mixing an x-liking orbital with an s orbital yields hybrids liking the x axis.

9. For equivalent hybrids (which is all that we consider) the orientation in space is determined by (a) the number of orbitals mixed and consequently the number of hybrids obtained, (b) which of the x, y, and z directions are preferred by the orbitals when "pure," and (c) the assumption that the electrons which will occupy the hybrids will try to avoid one another as far as possible within limitation b.   For example,

suppose we wish to form three equivalent hybrids by mixing the $2s$, $2p_x$, and $2p_y$ orbitals on an atom.   Condition b demands that their predominant directions lie in the xy plane; condition c divides the 360° of the xy plane into three parts, making the angle between hybrids 120°.

10. The particular type of hybrid chosen for a structure discussion is determined by the experimentally known geometry of the molecule.   (However, if it is not known, we still may make educated guesses about its shape by comparing it to related molecules.)   Bond angles of 120° should hint of sp^2 hybrids, linear systems of sp hybrids, and tetrahedral shapes or 109° bond angles of sp^3 hybrids.

4-8   THE NEON MOLECULAR ISOELECTRONIC SERIES

The rare-gas atom Ne and neighboring molecules HF, H_2O, NH_3, and CH_4 all have the same number of electrons (are isoelectronic), and all have the same *total* number of positive nu-

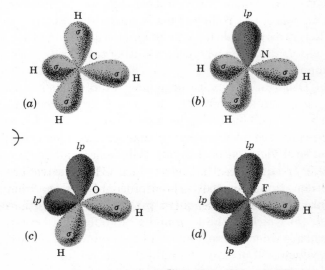

Fig. 4-19 sp^3 **models of CH_4, NH_3, H_2O, and HF.**

clear charges. The central atoms all have related external electronic structures; in going from C to Ne we simply fill the $2p$ level with its quota of electrons. Thus it is not surprising that the structures of these four molecules are similar. To illustrate this and to provide simultaneously the "better" picture of H_2O and NH_3 promised in Sec. 4-4, let us start with the tetrahedral picture of CH_4, a symmetrical molecule with four bond pairs separated by 109° bond angles (Fig. 4-19).

Imagine that we pluck one of the H nuclei (an H^+) from a σ bond in CH_4 and merge it with the carbon atom nucleus, increasing Z, the atomic number of carbon, by 1 and thus converting it to a nitrogen nucleus. The former bond pair is now a lone pair and overall what we now have is a NH_3 molecule (Fig. 4-19) still with the experimentally known pyramidal shape (determined by the nuclei) but now with bond angles of 109°. Thus the bond angle predicted by an sp^3 model of NH_3 is much closer to the experimentally known 106° than the p^3 model of Sec. 4-4 with its 90° angles.

Pushing another proton into the central nucleus gives us a water molecule with two σ bond pairs separated by 109° and two lone pairs completing the tetrahedron. One more proton push gives us HF, with three lone pairs and one σ bond.

Rationalizing the 109° perfect sp^3 bond angles down to 106° for NH_3 and 105° for H_2O is easy if we accept a rule ordering the strengths of pair-pair repulsions:

$$lp\text{-}lp \; > \; lp\text{-}bp \; > \; bp\text{-}bp$$

meaning that repulsion between lone pairs is greatest, repulsion between bond pairs the least. In CH_4 we have all bp-bp repulsions and a symmetrical molecule. In NH_3 we introduce one lp, and since lp-bp repulsion is greater than bp-bp repulsion, the bp's move together to escape the lp, thus decreasing the bond angle to 106°. Introducing another lp, in H_2O, decreases the angle further, to 105°.

The ordering rule presumably arises from the fact that lone-pair electron clouds, being bound to one nucleus only, generally puff out, become larger than the more localized bond-pair clouds, and consequently repel one another more. The rule is frequently of help in rationalizing small distortions from perfect symmetry.

Although the bond angle is a good criterion for choosing between the p^3 and sp^3 models for H_2O, we shall see in a later section on hydrogen bonding that molecular packing in ice confirms the tetrahedral distribution of electron pairs in H_2O. NH_3, between CH_4 and H_2O, thus seems well established as an sp^3 hybridized system. In the next section we shall employ this model in a discussion of one of its reactions.

4-9   OTHER SIMPLE MOLECULES

Before introducing more new concepts, we shall look at two or three examples of how to build molecular orbitals, emphasizing in this section "method of attack."

Consider the molecule H_2CO, formaldehyde, with the nuclear framework illustrated in Fig. 4-20a. Experiment tells us that this molecule is planar and that the angle between the two hydrogen atoms is slightly less than 120° (*Hint: sp^2 hybrids on carbon!*). With this knowledge in hand we can proceed to promote and hybridize the carbon to the $\phi_1{}^1 \phi_2{}^1 \phi_3{}^1 2p_z{}^1$ state, where the ϕ's are sp^2 hybrids in the xy plane, the plane of the molecule. We orient the hybrids toward O and H atoms, as in Fig. 4-20b. The oxygen atom has the configuration $1s^2 2s^2 2p_x{}^2 2p_y{}^1 2p_z{}^1$, and through overlap of its $2p_y$ AO with ϕ_3 of carbon a σ bond forms. The lone pair $2p_x$ on oxygen lies in the plane of the σ framework. ϕ_1 and ϕ_2 form σ bonds with hydrogens to complete the σ framework. Perpendicular to this plane, the $2p_z$ AO's on carbon and oxygen overlap sideways to form a π bond (Fig. 4-20c). The line formula with proper identification of bonds is shown in Fig. 4-20d, and the molecule is "finished."

A second method of attack, which will frequently prove useful when an electron-pairing scheme for a molecule is not immediately obvious, is the "reservoir" approach. Again consider formaldehyde—its shape and the hint of sp^2 hybridization. The external structures of atoms involved are

C: $1s^2\ 2s^2\ 2p^2$
O: $1s^2\ 2s^2\ 2p^4$
H: $1s^1$ (two of these)

Let us strip off all external electrons from these atoms (4 from carbon, 6 from oxygen, and 2 from the hydrogens) and put the 12 electrons in an imaginary electron reservoir or bucket while we deal with empty orbitals. Once again we construct sp^2 hybrids from carbon $2s$, $2p_x$, and $2p_y$ AO's and overlap two of them with hydrogen $1s$ AO's to form σ MO's (empty). We may construct sp hybrids on the oxygen atom (from the $2s$ and the $2p_y$ orbitals) and overlap one with the remaining sp^2 hybrid on carbon to form another empty σ MO. The empty σ frame-

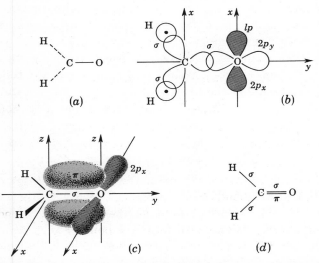

Fig. 4-20 Structure of the formaldehyde molecule. (a) **Position of the nuclei**; (b) **the σ structure**; (c) **the π structure**; (d) **line formula showing σ and π bonds.**

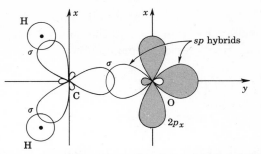

Fig. 4-21   The σ framework of formaldehyde with hybridized oxygen.

work (which includes every orbital located in the xy plane) is shown in Fig. 4-21.

(Actually in our previous method we could have hybridized the oxygen atom as we did here.   It is not necessary, but does have the advantage of removing the $2s$ oxygen electrons away from the bonding region, converting them to a lone pair. sp^2 hybrids on oxygen would also have been suitable.)

We now remove from our reservoir enough electrons to *fill completely* the σ framework.   (Generally we may assume that positions in the σ framework are more stable or are lower in energy than positions in the π structure.) We place 2 each in the C—H sigma bonds, 2 in the C—O sigma bond, 2 in the $lp\ 2p_x$ on oxygen, and 2 in the $lp\ sp$ hybrid on oxygen.   A total of 10 electrons are gone; 2 are left in the bucket and only 2 orbitals are left unused, $2p_z$ on carbon and $2p_z$ on oxygen.   We overlap these to form a π MO and fill it with the last 2 electrons.   The result is essentially the same as before (Fig. 4-20d).

Both the "pairing" and the "reservoir" methods have their advantages.   We recommend mastery of both.

Consider now the species BCl_3, which, as mentioned earlier, has no electric dipole moment.   Since B and Cl have different electronegativities, the B—Cl bonds are undoubtedly polar.   Thus if the molecule is not planar with 120° bond angles, μ would be something other than zero.   Now the configuration of boron is $1s^2\ 2s^2\ 2p_x^1$ and, upon promotion to p_y and sp^2 hy-

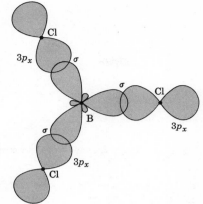

Fig. 4-22 The σ framework of BCl$_3$ (in the xy plane).

bridization, becomes $1s^2\ \phi_1{}^1\ \phi_2{}^1\ \phi_3{}^1$. Through overlap with a half-empty $3p$ orbital on each Cl we get three σ bonds, as shown in Fig. 4-22. Lone-pair $3p$ orbitals on Cl atoms are omitted. The structure is symmetrical and consistent with the absence of dipole moment in BCl$_3$. There is some possibility of π bonding through smearing of Cl $3p_z$ clouds into the empty $2p_z$ on boron, though this is probably not so likely in BCl$_3$ as in the species BF$_3$, where the orbitals are of comparable size.

Now consider the formation of the compound NH$_3$BF$_3$. We neglect any π smearing on BF$_3$ and assume that the structure is similar to BCl$_3$, with one largely empty $2p_z$ AO on boron. Recall the tetrahedral NH$_3$ (Fig. 4-19) with its lone pair. On the approach of the NH$_3$ lone pair (Fig. 4-23) the planar sp^2 BF$_3$ unit shifts into sp^3 hybridization, essentially pushing the empty orbital at the NH$_3$ lone pair and bending the B—F bonds back out of the way. B is now in the tetrahedral configuration $1s^2\ \phi_1{}^1\ \phi_2{}^1\ \phi_3{}^1\ \phi_4{}^0$, and the lp of NH$_3$ overlaps with the empty ϕ_4, forming a σ bond. Note that both electrons in this MO originally belonged to the nitrogen atom; for this reason the bond is sometimes called a "dative" bond (dative meaning "donating"). It is important to recognize, however, that once in the MO, the electrons do not know where they came from; a dative bond

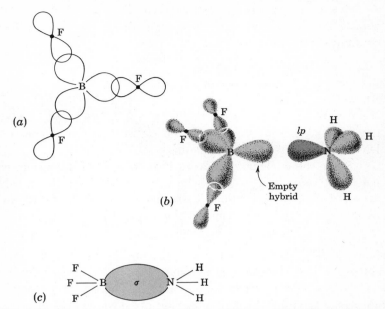

Fig. 4-23 **The formation of NH₃·BF₃.** (*a*) **Planar BF₃ with** sp^2 **hybrids on boron;** (*b*) **shift to** sp^3 **hybrids on approach of the NH₃ lone pair;** (*c*) **the dative** σ **bond.**

is a normal covalent bond, distinguished only by the mechanism of its formation.

4-10 DELOCALIZED π MOLECULAR ORBITALS

In all the molecules discussed so far the π *MO*'s were *localized* between two atoms, for example, between the two carbon atoms in ethylene in Fig. 4-17. Frequently, however, we encounter systems for which it is difficult to combine orbitals in the electron-pairing approach so that a unique set of π *MO*'s results. Then we must introduce the concept of *resonance* or delocalized π bonds. These ideas are easily illustrated with the SO₂ molecule.

SO$_2$ is nonlinear (recall that its dipole moment was not zero) with the nuclear framework suggested in Fig. 4-24a. The configurations of the isolated atoms are

S: $1s^2\ 2s^2\ 2p^6\ 3s^2\ 3p^4$
O: $1s^2\ 2s^2\ 2p^4$

We remove all electrons on sulfur with $n = 3$ and all on each oxygen with $n = 2$, placing a total of 18 in our reservoir and leaving all others as core electrons.

Since the nuclear framework hints of sp^2 hybridization, we construct these hybrids from the s, p_x, and p_y orbitals on each atom, overlap them in the xy plane, as shown in Fig. 4-24b, and assign 14 of our 18 electrons to the σ framework, 2 each in the two σ MO's and 10 as the lone pairs. Our 4 remaining electrons must be accommodated in the π framework built from the p_z

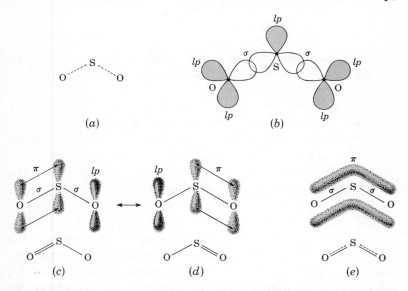

Fig. 4-24   Structure of the SO$_2$ molecule.   (a) Position of the nuclei; (b) σ framework in the xy plane; (c, d) the two resonance structures with localized π bonds; (e) the delocalized π cloud.   In (c), (d), and (e) the classical line formulas are shown below the orbital pictures.

orbitals perpendicular to the σ framework (Fig. 4-24c). But we find that we can do this in two entirely equivalent ways (Fig. 4-24c and d), with an lp on the right and a π MO on the left, or vice versa. Neither structure alone is adequate, for each predicts a molecule with one S—O linkage different from the other. Experiment says that SO_2 is symmetrical. If we want to retain the electron-pair picture, we must say that the true description of the molecule is something between these two pictures and denote this with a double-headed arrow placed between them. This particular type of arrow is associated with the term *resonance* and means *not* that the double bond flips from side to side but rather that the two forms are the best approximations that we can make to the true structure within the electron-pair model. A better picture for the π structure is shown in Fig. 4-24e, which can be regarded as a superposition of structures c and d. Here the π cloud appears *delocalized*, spread over three centers, and in the cloud (which is not a single MO, but a smear of MO's and AO's) there are wandering four π electrons. The dotted line in the structural formula for SO_2 is rapidly becoming popular in textbooks as a symbol for delocalized π bonds.

As a second example of delocalization we consider the molecule benzene, C_6H_6, which according to experiment is a planar molecule, with all 12 atoms in the same plane. The six carbon atoms are at the corners of a regular hexagon (Fig. 4-25a), each bonded to a single H atom located outside the hexagon. Assumption of sp^2 hybridization of each carbon easily leads to a σ framework containing 24 electrons (Fig. 4-25b).

On each carbon atom in the σ framework there remains one electron in a pure p orbital perpendicular to the trigonal hybrids and thus to the σ framework (Fig. 4-25c). Sideways overlap into localized π MO's can occur in two ways, illustrated with the line drawings in Fig. 4-25d. Since all the carbon-carbon bonds in benzene are equivalent, neither structure alone can be correct and we must employ the resonance arrow.

Alternatively, Fig. 4-25e shows the hexagonal doughnut-shaped clouds above and below the σ framework, obtained when the two localized π MO structures are superimposed.   The doughnuts accommodate the six π electrons (just as the three π MO's

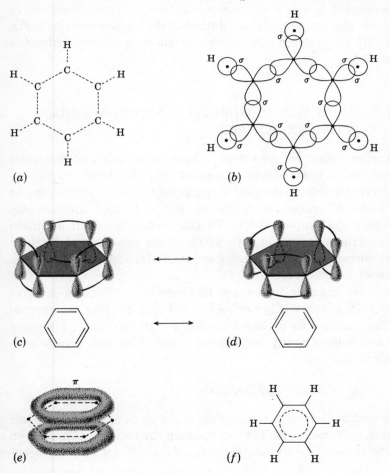

(a)

(b)

(c)

(d)

π

(e)

(f)

Fig. 4-25   The structure of the benzene molecule, C_6H_6.   (a) Position of the nuclei; (b) the σ framework; (c, d) the two resonance structures showing localized π bonds; (e) the delocalized π cloud; (f) line formula indicating delocalized π electrons by a dotted circle.

held a total of 6 electrons), and in these clouds the π electrons wander around, belonging now to no particular carbon atom and moreover to no particular *pair* of carbon atoms. The π electrons are "delocalized." Recognition of delocalization in benzene has led many recent authors of organic chemistry textbooks to adopt the "dotted-circle" representation (Fig. 4-25*f*) in preference to diagrams showing three localized π bonds.

4-11 A MORE DETAILED TREATMENT OF MOLECULAR ORBITALS IN DIATOMIC MOLECULES

Earlier, when we presented a naïve description of molecular orbitals in homonuclear molecules (H_2, N_2), based largely on electron-pairing concepts, we purposely avoided application to "problem" molecules, which cannot be treated satisfactorily within the simple model. In this section we shall outline a more rigorous approach to MO's, which can account for such problems: O_2 and its paramagnetism;† He_2 and its nonexistence under normal conditions.

We examine the oxygen molecule first. Experiment says that O_2 is essentially double-bonded and exhibits paramagnetism due to two unpaired electrons. In the simple approach we should start by considering isolated oxygen atoms with configurations

$$O: \quad 1s^2\, 2s^2\, 2p_x{}^2\, 2p_y{}^1\, 2p_z{}^1$$

according to Hund's rule. Taking the z axis as the internuclear axis, we form a σ MO by overlapping the two $2p_z$ AO's and, on appropriate orientation of the $2p_y$ AO's, form a π MO. Occu-

---

† Paramagnetism is the phenomenon associated with the behavior of molecules or solids containing unpaired electrons in the presence of a magnetic field. Attractive forces toward the field are exerted on the substance, and measurement of these (Chap. 6) enables us to estimate the number of unpaired electrons per molecule.

pation of the σ and π MO's corresponds to a normal double bond. However, we now have no unpaired electrons left to explain the paramagnetism. Retaining the double bond, we could resort to some rather artificial devices to obtain unpaired electrons, for example, exciting one electron from a $2p_x$ lone pair to a higher state; but the symmetry of the molecule argues against this. We could unpair the two $2p_x$ lp's, excite one electron from each into higher states, and then pair the remaining $2p_x$ ones in a π MO, but this approach seems to have little logic recommending it within the simple electron-pair approach.

In search of a more reasonable explanation let us recall the principles of hybridization. When mixing AO's *on one atom* to form hybrids, we always conserved the *number* of orbitals, for example, mixing four pure AO's gave four hybrid AO's, etc. In a sense we always conserved *allowed places for electrons to live*. A similar rule holds for the mixing of AO's on *different* atoms to form MO's. Let us reconsider the H_2 molecule with this in mind. Two $1s$ AO's merge as the molecule forms to produce a σ_{1s} MO of greater stability than either of the $1s$ AO's, and *also*, although we have neglected it thus far, a less-stable MO called the σ_{1s}^*. The relative energies of these are shown in Fig. 4-26.

The boundary diagram for the σ_{1s} MO has already been discussed (Fig. 4-27) and in three dimensions is rather ellipsoidal in shape.

The σ_{1s}^* MO has a boundary diagram possessing a nodal plane perpendicular to the z axis between the nuclei (Fig. 4-27), and the electron cloud is shifted away from the bonding region. Note that the MO is still σ in nature, for the nodal plane does not *contain* the internuclear axis. In three dimensions the MO is dumbbell-shaped. Because of the sparsity of the electron

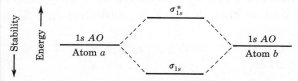

Fig. 4-26 Formation of bonding and antibonding MO's.

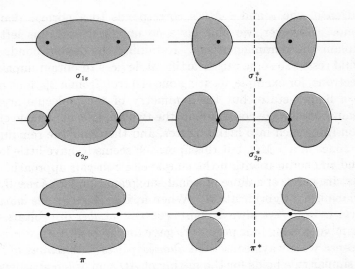

Fig. 4-27   Contour diagrams for bonding and antibonding σ_{1s}, σ_{2p}, and π molecular orbitals.

density between the nuclei and its higher energy, the σ_{1s}^* is called an *antibonding MO (ABMO)* to distinguish it from the bonding *MO (BMO)* σ_{1s}. Antibonding *MO*'s are usually marked with asterisks.

In general, *for homonuclear diatomic molecules* any two like *AO*'s can merge to form two *MO*'s, one of a bonding type more stable than the isolated *AO*'s and another of an antibonding type less stable than the isolated *AO*'s. For molecules larger than H_2, where the z direction is assumed to be the internuclear axis,

these AO's unite to form	*these MO's*
$2s_a$ and $2s_b$	σ_{2s} and σ_{2s}^*
$2p_{za}$ and $2p_{zb}$	σ_{2p} and σ_{2p}^*
$2p_{ya}$ and $2p_{yb}$	π_y and π_y^*
$2p_{xa}$ and $2p_{xb}$	π_x and π_x^*
$3s_a$ and $3s_b$	σ_{3s} and σ_{3s}^*

etc.

The shapes of the *BMO*'s have been discussed previously and are shown in Fig. 4-27 along with the *ABMO* contour diagrams.

For homonuclear diatomic molecules built of atoms of period 2 elements, an approximate ordering of the molecular energy levels is

$$\sigma_{1s} < \sigma_{1s}^* < \sigma_{2s} < \sigma_{2s}^* < \sigma_{2p} < \pi_x = \pi_y < \pi_x^* = \pi_y^* < \sigma_{2p}^*$$

π_x and π_y orbitals have the same sort of symmetry around the z axis, are geometrically equivalent, and consequently have the same energy.   Figure 4-28 shows these *MO* energies displayed in a diagram.   The spacings between the levels were chosen arbitrarily and are not meant to represent experimental energy differences.

Configurations of molecules can be found by applying the

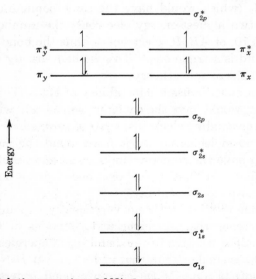

Fig. 4-28   Relative energies of *MO*'**s for diatomic molecules of period 2 atoms.   Occupation of these orbitals for the oxygen molecule is illustrated.**

Aufbau principle to this array of *MO's*. For O_2 (16 electrons) we have

$$O_2: \quad \sigma_{1s}^2 \; \sigma_{1s}^{*2} \; \sigma_{2s}^{'2} \; \sigma_{2s}^{*2} \; \sigma_{2p}^2 \; \pi_y^2 \; \pi_x^2 \; \pi_y^{*1} \; \pi_x^{*1}$$

The last two electrons enter the degenerate π_y^*-π_x^* level with spins unpaired according to Hund's rule, and thus the paramagnetism of O_2 is explained. To account for its double bond, we define a quantity called bond order *(BO)*, such that *BO's* of 0, 1, 2, and 3 correspond to classical no-bond, single, double, and triple bonds.

$BO = \frac{1}{2}$ (no. electrons in *BMO's*

$- $ no. electrons in *ABMO's*)

For O_2 there are 10 bonding electrons (with no asterisk) and 6 antibonding electrons (with asterisk); thus $BO = 2$, which corresponds to a double bond.

For N_2 (which would have the same configuration as O_2 minus the two highest-energy electrons) the number of *BMO* electrons is 10, of *ABMO* electrons 4; thus the bond order is 3, and the bond is a triple one. This we had already decided on the basis of the simpler theory.

We can now discuss the instability of He_2. This molecule (4 electrons) would have the configuration $\sigma_{1s}^2 \; \sigma_{1s}^{*2}$ with 2 bonding and 2 antibonding electrons, a *BO* of zero, corresponding to no bonds, no molecule. On the other hand the molecule-ion He_2^+ would have the configuration $\sigma_{1s}^2 \; \sigma_{1s}^{*1}$ and a net *BO* of $\frac{1}{2}$, corresponding to a "half-bond" or a one-electron bond. He_2^+ ions are known experimentally.

A rather classical problem very neatly explained by the *MO* theory concerns the dissociation energies of O_2 and its molecule-ion O_2^+ relative to the dissociation energies of N_2 and N_2^+. $D(O_2)$ is smaller than that of its ion, yet $D(N_2)$ is larger than that of its ion. If we compute bond orders for these species and recognize that the larger the *BO*, the more energy it will take to break the molecule in two, we see that O_2 with

$BO = 2$ *should* be dissociated with less energy than $O_2{}^+$ ($BO = 2\frac{1}{2}$). However, in going from N_2 ($BO = 3$) to its ion $N_2{}^+$, we remove an electron from a *BMO*, so that the ion *BO* is only $2\frac{1}{2}$. Thus $D(N_2) > D(N_2{}^+)$.

For heteronuclear diatomic molecules or molecule-ions in which the two atoms are not very different, for example, NO, OF, CN^-, the same theory can be applied reasonably well. NO, a paramagnetic molecule, has a *BO* of $\frac{5}{2}$ (a double bond plus a one-electron bond) according to the configuration:

$$\sigma_{1s}{}^2 \ \sigma_{1s}^{*2} \ \sigma_{2s}{}^2 \ \sigma_{2s}^{*2} \ \sigma_{2p}{}^2 \ \pi_x{}^2 \ \pi_y{}^2 \ \pi_x^{*1}$$

In general, the advanced theory contradicts none of our previous conclusions but allows us to treat systems for which the simpler electron-pair approach is inadequate.

4-12 HYBRIDS INVOLVING d ORBITALS

Three other types of hybrids are frequently useful in discussions of bonding in molecules containing atoms with d electrons or with low-lying empty d orbitals. We shall consider their properties briefly here and illustrate their use in Sec. 4-13.

Four dsp^2 hybrids of *square planar* symmetry may be constructed by mixing the $d_{x^2-y^2}$, s, p_x, and p_y orbitals. The four hybrids lie in the xy plane with neighboring lobes separated by 90°, as shown in Fig. 4-29. Each lobe represents one hybrid, and each may be used to form one σ bond.

Smearing of the d_{z^2} orbital, an s orbital, and all three p orbitals results in the five hybrids of *trigonal bipyramidal* sym-

Fig. 4-29 The four dsp^2 square planar hybrid orbitals.

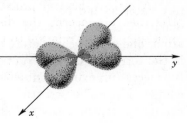

metry.   These dsp^3 hybrids are illustrated in Fig. 4-31a.   Normally the three hybrids in the xy plane are separated by 120°, while the remaining two are perpendicular to the xy plane.   A maximum of five σ bonds can be constructed with these.

Six *octahedral* d^2sp^3 hybrids are formed when the $d_{x^2-y^2}$, d_{z^2}, an s, and the three p orbitals are mixed.   These lie along the x, y, and z axes in plus and minus directions and can be used in construction of six σ bonds (Fig. 4-32a).

4-13   RARE-GAS AND INTERHALOGEN COMPOUNDS

With the discovery in 1962 of stable compounds of the higher rare gases, XeF_2, XeF_4, and XeF_6, chapters of many inorganic textbooks (harboring statements that rare gases have no tendency toward covalent-bond formation) were rendered out of date.   The announcement of these compounds shocked the orbital-believers, for the unusual stability of the "closed-shell" rare-gas configurations and their resistance to change had long been an accepted fact.   One writer (14) has aptly termed this acceptance the "closed-shell, closed-mind attitude" toward rare-gas chemistry.

For a long time certain *pseudo* compounds of the larger rare gases had been well known, for example, the crystalline hydrates such as $Xe \cdot 6H_2O$; but it was equally known that these are only *enclosure* or "cage" compounds; i.e., the rare-gas atoms are simply trapped or caged in the holes in the lattice of crystalline water and are not bound covalently.

It had seemed logical that any bona fide compound of the rare gases should be of the "addition" type, involving partial donation of a rare-gas electron pair to an electron-deficient atom, one with a completely empty external orbital like boron in the tetrahedral BF_3 structure of Fig. 4-23b.   Indeed several (unsuccessful) experiments had been attempted to prepare such compounds.   The structure of the xenon fluorides, however, cannot be satisfactorily explained by dative bonding.

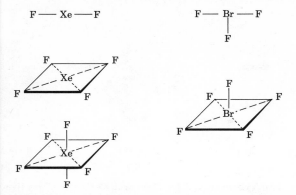

Fig. 4-30 The geometries of the three xenon fluorides and related interhalogens.

Theoreticians rapidly theorized, and shortly several different explanations of the bonding in these compounds were offered. Two of these involved no dramatic new ideas, but simply pointed out the similarity between the new compounds and the well-known *interhalogens* (compounds of halogens with other halogens) for which reasonable bonding theories already existed. Figure 4-30 illustrates with line drawings the shapes of a few of these molecules: the T-shaped interhalogen BrF_3, linear XeF_2, pyramidal BrF_5, square planar XeF_4, and octahedral XeF_6.

One of the suggested explanations calls for hybridization of orbitals on the central atom; therefore we begin by considering the ground-state electronic configurations of bromine and xenon.

Br $(Z = 35)$: $1s^2\ 2s^2\ 2p^6\ 3s^2\ 3p^6\ 3d^{10}\ 4s^2\ 4p^5\ [5s^0\ 5p^0\ 4d^0]$

Xe $(Z = 54)$: $1s^2\ 2s^2\ 2p^6\ 3s^2\ 3p^6\ 3d^{10}\ 4s^2\ 4p^6\ 4d^{10}\ 5s^2\ 5p^6$
$[6s^0\ 6p^0\ 5d^0]$

The bracketed empty orbitals are those next highest in energy in the isolated atoms.

We shall call on the lowest-energy *empty d* orbitals in Br and Xe to mix with the outermost filled s and p orbitals in

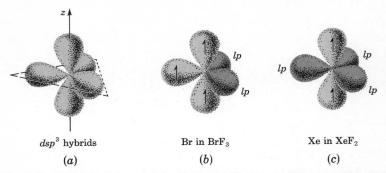

dsp^3 hybrids   Br in BrF_3 Xe in XeF_2

(a)   (b)   (c)

Fig. 4-31   The hybrid model for BrF₃ and XeF₂. (*a*) **The five trigonal bipyramidal** dsp^3 **hybrid orbitals;** (*b*) **the electron configuration of Br in BrF₃;** (*c*) **the electron configuration of Xe in XeF₂.**

forming the trigonal, bipyramidal dsp^3 hybrids illustrated in Fig. 4-31. Assignment of the seven external Br electrons as shown allows formation of three mutually perpendicular σ bonds by pairing with the lone $2p$ electron on fluorine. Two lone pairs (shaded orbitals) remain in the trigonal plane. Now, as we learned earlier in our discussions of H_2O, NH_3, and CH_4, electron-pair repulsions decrease in the order $lp\text{-}lp > lp\text{-}bp > bp\text{-}bp$. Accordingly we should expect the bond angles in BrF₃ to be less than 90°, and (comforting as it is) experiment says that the bond angles are approximately 87°.

For XeF₂ we assign the outer eight electrons to the hybrids as shown, so that the bond formation is consistent with the observed linear structure. The three lone pairs in the trigonal plane exert equivalent repulsion on both bond pairs; no distortion from linearity occurs.

For BrF₅, XeF₄, and XeF₆, construction of d^2sp^3 octahedral hybrids is indicated. Figure 4-32 shows the allocation of electrons appropriate for formation of pyramidal BrF₅ and square planar XeF₄. Again experiment reveals the distortional effect of $lp\text{-}bp$ repulsion in BrF₅; the four bonds represented as coplanar in Fig. 4-32*b* are bent slightly upward away from the lone pair. As expected, no such distortion is observed in XeF₄.

To explain XeF_6, we must postulate excitation of two electrons from the hybrids (leaving six unpaired) to some higher empty orbital, perhaps paired in the lower-lying $6s$, or unpaired in the degenerate $5d_{xy}$, $5d_{xz}$, or $5d_{yz}$ orbitals, which were not employed in hybrid construction. These d orbitals have lobe directions between the coordinate axes, avoiding the bond pairs. Magnetic studies should prove useful in establishing the identification of these excited electrons.

The hybridized model for the interhalogens and the xenon halides has been subjected to criticism on the grounds that an unreasonable amount of energy is necessary to bring about the hybridized states (the valence states) shown in Figs. 4-31 and 4-32. The relationship between this *excitation energy, bond-stabilization energy,* and *net bond energy* (the only *measurable* one of the three) is shown in Fig. 4-33. Within the electron-pairing model of bonding a certain amount of energy, the *promotional energy,* must be used up to prepare the central atom for bonding, i.e., excitation and reshuffling of electron densities in the hybridization process. Once the atom has been promoted to this excited state (a hypothetical one, indeed), bond formation takes place with attendant stabilization of the system, generally enough stabilization to compensate for the energy lost in promotion. The overcompensation is the net bond energy, the

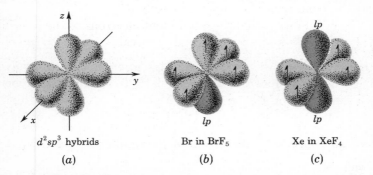

d^2sp^3 hybrids   Br in BrF_5 Xe in XeF_4

(a)   (b)   (c)

Fig. 4-32 The hybrid model for BrF_5 and XeF_4. (a) The six octahedral d^2sp^3 hybrids; (b) the electron configuration of Br in BrF_5; (c) the electron configuration of Xe in XeF_4.

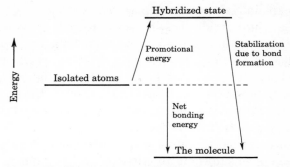

Fig. 4-33   Energy changes during bond formation.

energy which the experimentalist must supply to the molecule to tear it into its component atoms in their ground states.

Necessarily this two-step process of promotion and subsequent bond formation is fictional. The Br atom does not hover around in a d^2sp^3 state waiting for five fluorine atoms. Electron rearrangement and bonding take place simultaneously on the approach of the fluorine atoms, accompanied by the release of the *net* bond energy. The two-step idea is, however, a useful approach for analyzing the *intra*atomic and *inter*atomic contributions to the net bond energy.

The promotional energy P is usually computed by examining the experimental orbital energies of the *isolated* atoms, since there is no good way of assessing orbital energies when other atoms, about to bond, are in the vicinity. The promotional energy indicated for d-hybridized Br or Xe seems higher than usual. However, in view of the approximations involved in getting P, it does not seem reasonable to abandon the hybridization model on this account. Moreover, a somewhat higher P is consistent with a lower net bond energy; such is observed in both the interhalogen and rare-gas compounds.

The second popular explanation of the rare-gas–halogen bond requires the construction of a *three-center* σ bond, i.e., a delocalized σ *MO* system extending over three atoms. Figure

4-34 illustrates the proper orientation of orbitals for the MO's in linear XeF_2. Two fluorine p_z orbitals, each with one electron, overlap in a straight line with the filled $5p_z$ AO on Xe. Smearing of all three atomic orbitals yields three MO's, one that is bonding with respect to the isolated orbitals, one antibonding, and the third *nonbonding*. A nonbonding molecular orbital ($NBMO$) has an energy like those of the isolated atomic orbitals, and no bond stability is gained or lost when an electron occupies it. Consequently, if the four electrons originally in the isolated AO's are assigned two each to the BMO and $NBMO$, a small net stabilization results, roughly equivalent to that of one σ bond *over all three atoms* or one-half a σ bond between Xe and each fluorine. Thus again a weak bond energy is predicted.

The structures of XeF_4 and XeF_6 (and of all the interhalogens) are explained by postulating the formation of mutually perpendicular delocalized σ MO's. XeF_6, for example, would have these three-center MO's along the x, y, and z directions.

The molecular-orbital method avoids all arguments about promotional energy, since it requires no excitation of electrons to higher-energy d orbitals. Also, in this approach there is no question of possible unpaired electrons in XeF_6.

At present it is difficult to decide which method more closely approaches the "truth" about bonding in rare-gas compounds. However, scientists all over the world have plunged into this exciting new field of chemistry, and experiments and calculations even now in progress are bound to clarify questions of their structure.

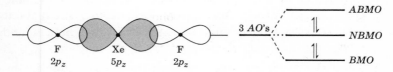

Fig. 4-34   The three-center–four-electron MO model of XeF_2.

EXERCISES

1 Discuss the nature of bonding in the molecules H_2S, PH_3, SiH_4, and P_2. Be specific about bond angles, number of σ and π bonds, lone pairs, type of hybridization, and cores.

2 Consider the molecule acetylene, C_2H_2, which is linear. Discuss the type of hybridization, types of bonds, and electron distributions likely for this molecule. Draw a contour diagram representing a cross section perpendicular to the internuclear axis of the "finished" molecule.

3 Compute the percent ionic character of the molecules HCl, HBr, and HI.

4 Discuss the nature of the bonding in the molecule H_2O_2. A skeleton drawing of it is: $H{-}O{-}O{-}H$ Would the molecule be planar?

5 The molecule CO_2 is linear with the carbon atom between the oxygens. Discuss with pictures the probable bonding in this molecule. Draw a classical line structure consistent with your model.

6 Suggest why in many textbooks the negative charge on the linear cyanate ion OCN^- is written near the nitrogen end of the ion.

7 Suggest on the basis of orbital theory two possible geometric structures for the molecule P_4. The four phosphorus atoms are equivalent.

8 Consider the molecule and molecule-ions OF, OF^-, and OF^+. Discuss their bond orders (and make a guess about their respective bond lengths), possible paramagnetism, and respective dissociation energies.

9 The $CO_3^=$ ion is a planar one with the carbon atom in the center of a triangle formed by the oxygens. Discuss the bonding in this molecule.

10 NO_2 and N_2O are molecules with the frameworks (bent) $O^{\diagdown N \diagup}O$ and (linear) N—N—O, respectively. Discuss the bonding in these molecules. Would any paramagnetism be expected?

11 The molecule borazole $B_3N_3H_6$ has the framework:

Discuss the bonding in this molecule.

$$
\begin{array}{c}
H \\
| \\
H\diagdown_{N}\diagup^{B}\diagdown_{N}\diagup H \\
| \quad\quad | \\
B\diagdown_{N}\diagup B \\
H\diagup \quad | \quad \diagdown H \\
H
\end{array}
$$

12 Suggest a possible orbital structure for the rare-gas compound $XeOF_4$.

13 Discuss reasons why the compound OF_6 has never been observed, while SF_6, in principle a member of the same family of compounds, is known.

14 Figure 4-35 shows one representation of the tetrahedral CH_4 molecule. The four H atoms are located at the four corners of a cube, and the carbon atom is at the origin of the coordinate system. Express the bond dipole-moment vectors in terms of their components along the x, y, and z axes and show that their sum is zero, i.e., that the resultant dipole moment of CH_4 is zero.

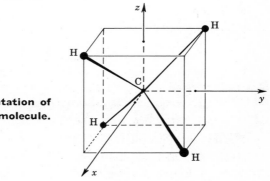

Fig. 4-35   A representation of the tetrahedral CH_4 molecule.

15 The nitric acid molecule has the planar framework $\begin{smallmatrix} O' \\ \diagdown \\ O' \diagup \end{smallmatrix} N-O \diagup^H$ where angle O'—N—O' is 130° and angle O'—N—O is 115°. Angle N—O—H is not well established but is known to be not 180°. The N—O distance is longer than the equivalent N—O' distances, and there is some probable restricted rotation of the OH group with respect to the NO_2 group. Propose an orbital model for the molecule consistent with all these facts.

REFERENCES

1 R. B. Heslop and P. L. Robinson, "Inorganic Chemistry," chaps. 5, 6, Elsevier Publishing Company, Amsterdam, 1960.

2 E. Cartmell and G. W. A. Fowles, "Valency and Molecular Structure," chap. 9, Butterworth & Co. (Publishers), Ltd., London, 1956.

3 L. Pauling, "The Nature of the Chemical Bond," 3d ed., Cornell University Press, Ithaca, N.Y., 1960.

4 E. S. Gould, "Inorganic Reactions and Structure," rev. ed., chap. 25, part II, Holt, Rinehart and Winston, Inc., New York, 1962.

5 G. W. A. Fowles, Lone Pair Electrons, *J. Chem. Educ.*, **34**, 187 (1957).

6 C. R. Noller, A Physical Picture of Covalent Bonding and Resonance in Organic Chemistry, *J. Chem. Educ.*, **27**, 504 (1950).   See also *J. Chem. Educ.*, **32**, 23 (1955).

7 H. Alyea, Potential Energy Curves in General Chemistry, *J. Chem. Educ.*, **19**, 337 (1962).

8 I. Cohen, The Shape of the $2p$ and Related Orbitals, *J. Chem. Educ.*, **38**, 20 (1961).

9 T. McCullough, Simple Calculation of the Tetrahedral Bond Angle, *J. Chem. Educ.*, **39**, 476 (1962).

10 E. A. Ogryzlo and G. B. Porter, Contour Surfaces for Atomic and Molecular Orbitals, *J. Chem. Educ.*, **40**, 256 (1963).

11 W. E. Dascent, Non-existent Compounds, *J. Chem. Educ.*, **40**, 130 (1963).

12 R. Ward, Would Mendeleev Have Predicted the Existence of XeF_4? *J. Chem. Educ.*, **40**, 277 (1963).

13 A. R. von Hippel, Molecular Designing of Materials, *Science*, **138**, 91 (1962).

14 C. L. Chernick, Chemical Compounds of the Noble Gases, *Record Chem. Progr. Kresge-Hooker Sci. Lib.*, **24**, 139 (1963).

15 C. A. Coulson, "Valence," 2d ed., sec. 6.3, Oxford University Press, Fair Lawn, N.J., 1961.

16 D. Halliday and R. Resnick, "Physics for Students of Science and Engineering," 2d ed., part II, sec. 30-4, John Wiley & Sons, Inc., New York, 1962.

IONIC, METALLIC, AND VAN DER WAALS BONDING

5

5-1 IONIC BONDING; STABILIZATION OF IONS IN CRYSTALS

Earlier we said that atoms whose external electronic configurations were similar to those of the rare gases (atoms on the far right or far left of the periodic table) tend to attain the rare-gas configuration by losing or gaining electrons, as appropriate. However, if we examine the energy relationships accompanying such processes for the isolated atoms, this statement at first seems unreasonable. Consider a system containing 1 *mole* of gaseous Na atoms separated from 1 *mole* of gaseous Cl atoms. If we supply to the system an amount of energy I_1, the first ionization energy of Na, we can effect the process:

$$I_1 + Na \rightarrow Na^+ + e^-$$

For a mole of Na atoms I_1 is 118.6 kcal.

If 1 mole of electrons is supplied to the Cl atoms in the system, energy equal to the electron affinity (EA) of Cl is released. The electron affinity of Cl is 92.5 kcal/mole.

$$e^- + Cl \rightarrow Cl^- + EA$$

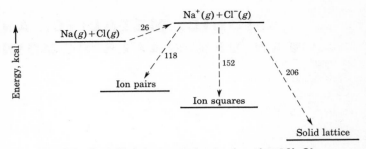

Fig. 5-1   Stabilization energies for 1 mole of NaCl.

Thus for the creation of ions in the gas phase, assuming no interaction between ions as yet, we must expend 26.1 kcal of work:

$$26.1 \text{ kcal} + Na + Cl \rightarrow Na^+ + Cl^-$$

Therefore in Fig. 5-1 the state of the system of isolated ions is shown as a *less* stable one compared to the isolated atoms. The factor rescuing us from this unpleasant situation is that ions, as charged particles, attract one another according to Coulomb's law, gaining *per single ion pair* a classical electrostatic stabilization energy given by

$$E_{ip} = \frac{(+z_c)(-z_a)e^2}{r}$$

where z_c and z_a are integers characteristic of the positive ion (the cation) and the negative ion (the anion), $+z_c e$ is the total charge on the cation (expressed as a multiple of the electron charge e), and r is a variable distance separating the ions, treated as point charges. We see that, as the separation decreases, the stabilization energy of a pair increases, and in fact reaches its maximum when the two ions merge to a point. Even though we treat the ions as point charges when discussing their attraction, we recognize their finite size by assuming that there is a distance of closest approach, d (Fig. 5-2), decided when the outer filled orbitals of the ions begin bumping one

another and repelling.   In a sense the peculiar stability of the
rare-gas configurations allows us to think of the ions as though
they were hard spheres, at least to a first approximation.
Balance between electrostatic attraction and electronic repulsion causes an equilibrium interionic distance to be established,
reminiscent of the equilibrium distance between atoms in molecules.   For a Na^+—Cl^- pair, the gas phase d is 2.814 Å.   With
the convenient conversion factor $Ne^2/1$ Å $= 331.0$ kcal we can
express the single-ion-pair energy as

$$E_{ip}(NaCl) = \frac{(+1)(-1)e^2}{2.814 \text{ Å}} = \frac{-117.9}{N} \text{ kcal}$$

where N is Avogadro's number.
    The 1 mole of Na^+ and 1 mole of Cl^- in our system are
sufficient to form 1 mole, or N single ion pairs.   Thus the total
stabilization energy due to pair formation, U_{ip}, can be computed as

$$U_{ip} = NE_{ip} = -117.9 \text{ kcal}$$

enough to bring our system into a state *more* stable than the
isolated atoms (Fig. 5-1).
    If two ion pairs cluster together to form an ion square
(Fig. 5-3), the stabilization energy increases.   For a single ion
square we have

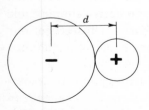

Fig. 5-2   Ion-pair
formation.

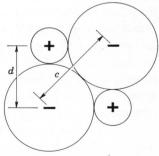

Fig. 5-3   Ion-square formation. $c = \sqrt{2}d$.

$$E_{is} = \frac{4(+1)(-1)e^2}{d} + \frac{(+1)(+1)e^2}{\sqrt{2}\,d} + \frac{(-1)(-1)e^2}{\sqrt{2}\,d}$$

$$= \frac{2(1.293)e^2}{d} = 2(1.293)E_{ip}$$

In our assembly of ions we have $N/2$ such ion squares possible, so that the total stabilization energy due to ion-square formation, U_{is}, is

$$U_{is} = \frac{N}{2}E_{is} = 1.293NE_{ip} = -152.4 \text{ kcal}$$

When *all* the ions in our assembly are brought together in a single cluster, conceivably built by lining up ion squares in all directions, the result is macroscopic crystalline solid NaCl, a three-dimensional *lattice* of ions.   As one might expect, the resulting stabilization is even greater than that in the ion-square case.   The stabilizing energy U_L is known as the lattice energy of the solid and is always expressible in terms of a constant A_M (known as the Madelung constant), the Avogadro number N, and the single-ion-pair energy:

$$U_L = A_M N E_{ip}$$

The Madelung constant for a solid is analogous to the constant 1.293 which we obtained for ion squares, and is computed in a manner somewhat similar, by summing interactions in all directions in the solid until the sum converges.   Logically then, the Madelung constant will depend upon *how* the ions cluster together, upon the geometry of the crystal.   For solids which crystallize like NaCl (square upon square to form a simple cubic structure) the Madelung constant is 1.7476.   Thus U_L for our mole of NaCl is 206 kcal.   Figure 5-1 shows the total stabilization gained.

For a more complete picture of the energy effects accompanying the formation of an ionic solid from the elements *in their natural states* we would indicate in Fig. 5-1 the energy necessary to convert the solid metal to gaseous atoms (the heat of sublimation of the metal) and the energy required to create the anion-to-be (in the case of chlorine, the dissociation energy of molecular Cl_2 gas).

The lattice energy represents to a first approximation the binding energy of the ions in the crystal. More rigorous treatments account for the fact that ions are not really point charges or even hard spheres, but rather squashable species; these effects introduce relatively small corrections to the electrostatic energy.

The magnitude of the lattice energy has significant influence on certain physical properties of a solid: for example, its melting point, its solubility. NaCl and KCl, which have like crystal structures, have melting points 801 and 768°C, respectively, the small decrease being due to increase in d and consequent decrease in U_L. MgO, also of simple cubic structure, melts at 2800°C, owing partly to decrease in d, but primarily to increase in ionic charge. From examination of the single-ion-pair formula we see that E_{ip} (and consequently U_L) increases fourfold when ionic charge increases from 1 to 2.

Solubility differences among salts may be related to the differences between their lattice energies and the so-called hydration energies of ions in solution. Positive ions in a water environment may gain a stabilization energy by attracting to them the lone-pair oxygen electrons of water molecules. Indeed this electrostatic binding is so strong that, as the cations wander through the solution, the water molecules are dragged along with them. Anions achieve a similar stabilization by attraction to the hydrogen atoms in the water molecule. Because of unequal sharing of electrons in the O—H bond (O is more electronegative), the H atom is almost a bare proton, a bare positive charge sitting on the end of the OH sigma MO. The anion moves up to it and achieves stabilization through electrostatic attraction.

At the surface of a crystal immersed in water there rages a contest between lattice stabilization and hydration stabilization. If the latter is greater, the crystal dissolves.

The possibility of hydration stabilization accounts for the greater water solubility of most ionic compounds compared to covalent molecules.

5-2 SIZE OF IONS

Thus far we have implied that ions, regarded as hard spheres in crystalline solids, have a measurable size; yet this is not strictly true.   We *can* measure the distance between ion centers in a solid by means of X-ray diffraction (see Chap. 1).   With a known wavelength of X-radiation, measurement of the angles through which the beam is bent allows us to calculate the distance between the ion centers.   To get a measure of the radius of the hard sphere, we must resort to more devious means. Consider the solid LiBr, and assume that we have learned from X-ray studies how the ions are positioned in the crystal (in our familiar simple cubic) and the distances between ion centers. The Li^+ ion, with only two electrons, would be smaller than Br^- with 36 electrons, so that we could safely assume that the packing in LiBr was largely determined by the Br^- ions, as shown in Fig. 5-4.   One-half the measurable distance d can be taken as the radius of the bromide ion.   One may then, through a similar study of KBr, where the ions are of comparable size (Fig. 5-4), determine r_{K^+} by subtraction of r_{Br^-} from the meas-

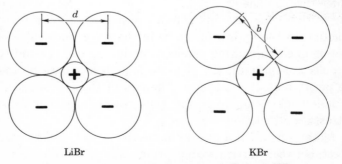

LiBr   KBr

Fig. 5-4   Packing of spheres in LiBr and KBr.

urable distance b.   The amazing thing is that these radii, so determined, appear to be reasonably constant from compound to compound.   For example, if one determined r_{I^-} with solid LiI and proceeded through KI to get r_{K^+}, the value obtained is very close to that of the bromide study.   Through paths like

Table 5-1   Some Representative Averaged Ionic Radii (in Angstroms)

									H^-	2.08
Li^+	0.60	Be^{++}	0.31				$O^=$	1.40	F^-	1.36
Na^+	0.95	Mg^{++}	0.65	Al^{3+}	0.50		$S^=$	1.84	Cl^-	1.81
K^+	1.33	Ca^{++}	0.99				$Se^=$	1.98	Br^-	1.95
Rb^+	1.48	Sr^{++}	1.12				$Te^=$	2.21	I^-	2.16
Cs^+	1.69	Ba^{++}	1.35							

Ti^{++}	V^{++}	Cr^{++}	Mn^{++}	Fe^{++}	Co^{++}	Ni^{++}	Cu^{++}	Zn^{++}
0.90	0.88	0.84	0.80	0.76	0.74	0.69	0.72	0.74

Bi^{3+}	0.96		Sc^{3+}	0.81		Mn^{3+}	0.66		Si^{4+}	0.42
Cr^{6+}	0.52		Cu^+	0.96		Ce^{4+}	1.01		Ti^{4+}	0.68

these taken over most of the periodic table it is possible to set up a self-consistent set of *averaged* ionic radii, a representative sample of which is shown in Table 5-1.   The constancy of ionic radii enables us to make many valuable predictions about crystal structure.

5-3 TRENDS IN IONIC RADII

The patterns apparent in Table 5-1 are easily explained in terms of our concepts of orbital theory and are quickly classified in terms of four general rules.

Rule 1

For an isoelectronic series (a series of ions with the same number of electrons) size decreases with increase in atomic number.

This is simply the effect of increased nuclear attraction for the electron cloud.

$$r_{Mg^{++}} < r_{Na^+} < r_{F^-} < r_{O^-}$$

Rule 2

Members of a family increase in size as we travel down the periodic table, a consequence of adding electrons with their most probable distance farther from the nucleus.

$$r_{F^-} < r_{Cl^-} < r_{Br^-} < r_{I^-}$$

Rule 3

For cations of the same element, size decreases with ionic charge because there are fewer electrons. Example: $r_{Fe^{++}} = 0.76$ Å; $r_{Fe^{3+}} = 0.64$ Å. The reverse holds true for anions, though anions with variable charge are less common.

Rule 4

Ions of comparable charge of transition elements (Ti^{++} to Ni^{++}, for example) have less dramatic changes in radii with increase in atomic number (see Table 5-1). Addition of a proton to the nucleus and an electron to the d orbitals seems to be an almost compensatory process.

5-4 RADIUS RATIO AND PACKING OF IONS IN CRYSTALS

The concept of radius ratio enables us to apply our tables of ionic radii to qualitative prediction of how ions are most likely to be clustered in crystals and what are most probably the formulas of certain clusters of ions, i.e., complex ions, found in solutions. First we define coordination number (CN) of an ion as the number of nearest neighbors around it. If ion A is surrounded by three B ions in a planar trigonal configuration, its CN is 3.   If its neighbors have square planar or tetrahedral symmetry, its CN is 4.   Other arrangements are mentioned in Table 5-2.

Table 5-2   Radius Ratio and Coordination Number

R_r	CN	Symmetry
< 0.155	1 or 2	Linear or bent molecules
0.155–0.225	3	Trigonal planar environment of A
0.225–0.414	4	Tetrahedral environment of A
0.414–0.732	4	Square planar environment of A
0.414–0.732	6	Octahedral environment of A (example, NaCl)
0.732–1.0	8	Body-centered-cubic, or twisted-cubic environment of A
> 1.0	12	Close-packed structure of metals where all atoms are alike

The radius ratio R_r for a binary ionic solid CA is defined as r_c/r_a, where r_c and r_a are ionic radii of cation and anion. Now, obviously, within the hard-sphere approximation, as the cation becomes larger with respect to the anion (as R_r increases), more anions can fit around the cation; i.e., the CN of the cation may increase.   Table 5-2 shows the possible CN for various radius ratios as computed from simple geometric considerations about sphere packing. Armed with these, we can make simple (but not infallible) predictions.   Suppose that we know that beryllium ion in solution forms a complex ion with the fluoride ion of formula $[BeF_n]^{(n-2)-}$.   Computing R_r for Be^{++} and F^-, we obtain 0.232, which indicates a tetrahedral $BeF_4^=$ ion, perhaps fortuitously in agreement with experiment.   For solid NaCl, R_r is 0.525, consistent with $CN = 6$ and a simple cubic structure.   For CsCl we obtain an R_r of 0.934, in agreement with the CN of 8 and body-centered-cubic structure known experimentally.   The radius-ratio concept is generally more successful when applied to solids than to complex ions in solution, but in all cases we are limited by the fact that ionic radii themselves vary somewhat with coordination number.

5-5 IONIC POTENTIAL AND PARTIAL COVALENCY

A second useful (but again not infallible) concept involving ionic radii is that of ionic potential, which enables us to rationalize discrepancies between theoretical predictions based on perfect ionic character and experimental results.

The ionic potential† (IP) of an ion is defined as

$$IP = \frac{z_c}{r_c}$$

where z_c is the ion charge expressed as an integral multiple of e, the electron charge.

Cations with a large ionic potential have considerable *polarizing power*, or ability to distort neighboring electron clouds toward them, thus inducing *partial covalence*. Consequently, comparison of ionic potentials allows us to make qualitative comparisons of degrees of covalence. For example, the oxide of sodium, Na_2O, is considered to be more ionic than its neighbor MgO. The IP for Na^+ is $1/0.95$ or 1.05, while that of Mg^{++} is $2/0.65$ or 3.08.

The trend in thermal stabilities of alkaline-earth carbonates can be explained in terms of the metal ionic potentials. When heated, these compounds undergo the reaction

$$MCO_3 \rightarrow MO + CO_2$$

† The term ionic potential should be distinguished from the misused term *ionization potential*. Unfortunately, *ionization potential* is the name given to the *ionization energy* in many texts. Ionization energy (I) is the energy (in electron volts, kilocalories per mole, etc.) necessary to remove an electron from an atom or molecule; ionic potential (IP) is a defined, nonexperimental quantity with the true dimensions of an electrostatic potential, i.e., charge per unit distance.

$BaCO_3$ decomposes at 1360°C; the others in the family decompose at gradually lower temperatures, down to less than 100°C for $BeCO_3$. In the crystalline solid the M^{++} ion is surrounded by the oxygens of the $CO_3^=$ ion, and when the metal ionic potential is large [$IP(Be^{++}) = 6.5$; $IP(Ba^{++}) = 1.6$], a partial covalent bond is formed between the metal and an oxygen atom, weakening the associated C—O bond by electron withdrawal. The result is easy decomposition to MO and CO_2.

5-6 METALLIC BONDING; INTRODUCTION

A quick review of some of the experimentally observed properties of metals tells us that the nature of the glue holding together atoms in a metal is indeed paradoxical. First, metals are crystalline solids with all lattice sites occupied by identical atoms. Obviously these *atoms* cannot be bound by purely electrostatic forces like those between cations and anions in an ionic crystal. Van der Waals forces (see Sec. 5·9) are much too weak to account for the high melting points of metals. Furthermore, each atom in the metal has 12 to 14 near neighbors, far too many to make palatable any postulate of localized covalent bonds. Then too, metals possess the unique properties called malleability and ductility characteristic of few ionic *or* covalent substances.

5-7 BAND THEORY OF METALS

We find the first real hint of the true nature of metallic binding in the exceptionally high electrical conductivity of metals. If a piece of metal is connected to the poles of a battery, a current will flow, suggesting the presence of loosely bound (delocalized) metal electrons that can be made to move. Let us search the electronic configurations of some common metal atoms for the electrons most likely to be delocalized and consequently mobilized. Here are three typical metals:

Na $(Z = 11)$:   (neon core)[10] $3s^1$

Fe $(Z = 26)$:   (argon core)[18] $3d^6$ $4s^2$

Ag $(Z = 47)$:   (krypton core)[36] $4d^{10}$ $5s^1$

These atoms, and most other metallic atoms, are characterized by having s electrons external to filled (or partially filled) inner shells. We select these s electrons for delocalization, partly because they are most easily ionized and partly because of their diffuseness. They occupy a large volume in space relative to other electrons and present an overall low electron density to the positive nucleus. To illustrate this latter point, suppose we compare the radius of the normal atom with the radius of the ion formed by removing the s electrons: Na, 1.57 Å, Na$^+$, 0.95 Å; Fe, 1.16 Å, Fe^{++}, 0.76 Å; Ag, 1.34 Å, Ag$^+$, 1.26 Å. Since the volume of the atom or ion varies as the cube of the radius, these changes reflect rather large changes in volume and show that the s electrons are indeed spread out in space.

For a very simple model we shall assume that the lattice sites in the metal crystal are held by the relatively small positive ionic cores (Na$^+$, Fe^{++}) and that these are surrounded by loosely bound delocalized s electrons whose orbitals are overlapping in all directions, forming what may be considered a gigantic MO extending over the whole crystal. The s electrons are thus shared with all the cores in the crystal. Within the wave interpretation of the electron, they are smeared around the cores, flowing in all directions. Within the particle interpretation, they are buzzing around the cores, with all directions equally probable. Because there is no net movement of electrons in any particular direction, there is no net flow of current in the isolated normal metal.

The delocalization of electron *position* in *xyz* coordinate space brings about what one may call a delocalization of the electron *quantum levels* in energy space (an abstract, but useful concept). Consider Fig. 5-5, where we illustrate first the discrete energy level of a particular orbital on an isolated atom (a one-center system, the center being the nucleus). In Chap. 4

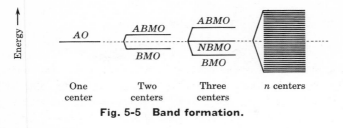

Fig. 5-5   Band formation.

we learned that, when a diatomic molecule is formed (a two-center system), two AO's of equal energy combined to give two MO's, one bonding and one antibonding, each with its own discrete energy.   For three centers, as in XeF_2, we mixed three AO's and obtained three MO's, with BMO, $ABMO$, and $NBMO$ energy levels.   For n centers, where n is very large, we obtain n distinct energy levels.

In a metallic crystal, where n is of the order of 10^{23}, the discrete level which corresponded to a $4s$ electron, for example, is smeared by the overlap of many $4s$ orbitals into a "band" of levels, which experimentally appears to be a continuum and is consequently called a "quasi continuum."   The differences between the very closely spaced energy levels in the band cannot be detected.   Each of the 10^{23} or more s electrons has one of the energies comprising this band, but we cannot say specifically which energy.   The discreteness of the isolated level is lost by delocalization or "broadening."

The electron capacity of a band is n (the number of atoms in the crystal) times the capacity of the parent discrete level, since n "quasi levels" exist within the band.   For example, if there are 10^{23} atoms in the crystal, the $2p$ band can accommodate 6×10^{23} electrons.   Within this band the electrons will occupy the states of lowest energy or greatest stability.   In sodium metal, for example, the bottom half of the $3s$ band will be filled with electrons, while the top half remains relatively uninhabited.

Figure 5-6 indicates that even the energy levels of "core" electrons are broadened somewhat in the solid, but that widths

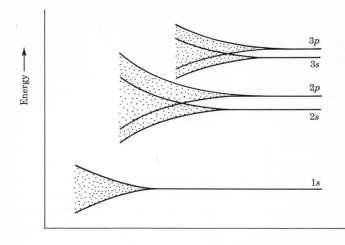

Internuclear distance ⟶

Fig. 5-6 Band broadening in solids as a function of internuclear distance.

of the resulting bands are small compared to those of external overlapping orbitals. If the discrete energy levels are well separated in the isolated atoms, little merging of bands due to broadening occurs in the metal. On the other hand, levels which are very close in energy in the atoms will most likely have merging bands when the internuclear distance decreases from large R to the equilibrium distance R_e in the metal. Note in Fig. 5-6 how the $3s$ and $3p$ bands merge as the atoms are squashed together. Between the bands are energy gaps which are forbidden to the electrons, just as energy spaces between discrete orbital levels are forbidden in the isolated atoms.

5-8 CONDUCTORS, SEMICONDUCTORS, AND INSULATORS

With the simple models provided by this theory we can easily explain why some substances are good conductors of electricity and others are insulators (nonconductors). Let us consider two fictitious solids A and B, whose band systems are shown in Fig. 5-7.

If we connect our solid sample (either A or B) to the poles of a battery, the electrons in the solid will feel a potential difference across the sample.   In order for a current to flow, there must be a net flow of electrons through the solid, completing the circuit.   As we stated before, in a metal electrons are flowing equally probably in all directions.   When the solid is placed in the circuit, the electrons will increase their energy of motion in the direction of the positive pole of the battery, *provided that* there are empty states within the uppermost inhabited band to accommodate this increase in energy.   In the solid A (Fig. 5-7) electrons can be excited by the electric field to nearby empty levels in the same band, and then can move preferentially toward the positive pole.   Solid A is consequently a conductor. If there are no empty levels in the topmost band, electrons cannot gain energy in any particular direction, there is no net flow, and the solid is an insulator (case B).

An insulator sometimes may be made to conduct by application of a potential so large that electrons are excited across the forbidden energy gap into the next highest band.   Such a phenomenon is called dielectric breakdown.

Besides metals and insulators the class of substances called semiconductors can be discussed in terms of bands.   Conductivity in these solids, unlike that of the true metals, increases as temperature increases.   An "intrinsic" semiconductor is a

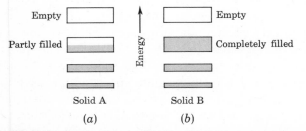

Fig. 5-7   **Electron occupation in the bands of** (a) **a conductor;** (b) **an insulator.**

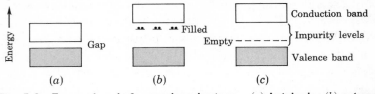

Fig. 5-8   Energy bands for semiconductors.   (a) **Intrinsic;** (b) n-**type;**
(c) p-**type.**

pure substance whose topmost band (called the valence band),
though filled, is separated from an empty band by a relatively
small forbidden energy gap (Fig. 5-8a).   As the temperature is
increased, electrons absorbing heat are excited across the small
gap and enter the previously empty "conduction" band, where
they may respond to an electric potential and cause a flow of
current.

Sometimes substances which are normally insulators can
become semiconducting upon introduction of small amounts of
impurity atoms into the lattice.   These are called "extrinsic"
semiconductors.   To explain their behavior, we assume that
energy levels due to the impurity atoms locate within the forbidden energy gap of the insulator (Fig. 5-8b and c), and, because very little overlap occurs between the orbitals of the
foreign atoms, are very nearly discrete.   The lattice orbitals,
having much different energies, do not mix with them.   For an
n-type semiconductor, it is necessary to assume that *filled* impurity levels are situated quite close to the conduction band
and that thermal excitation of these impurity electrons to the
conduction band enables current to flow. n-type semiconductors are formed when an impurity atom possesses more external
electrons than the parent insulator atoms, for example, arsenic
or phosphorus atoms (Group V) in solid silicon (Group IV).
In contrast, a p-type semiconductor contains as impurities
atoms with *fewer* external electrons than the parent insulator
atoms, for example, boron (Group III) in solid silicon (Group
IV).   In this case, *empty* impurity levels must exist quite close
to the silicon *valence* band.   When silicon electrons are ther-

mally excited to the impurity states, the vacancies (positive holes) created in the valence band can be excited by an electric field with consequent current flow due to flow of *holes!*

5-9 THE NATURE OF VAN DER WAALS FORCES

Of all the forces playing a role on the molecular stage those termed van der Waals forces are no doubt the weakest though probably the most universal. Associated with energies of only about 1 to 10 kcal/mole, they are usually masked by the stronger covalent forces (with energies of about 100 kcal/mole) present in molecules. Their role is important only in explaining interactions between molecules and atoms with "saturated" orbitals, where no covalent bonding is likely.

As early as 1873 Diderick van der Waals recognized the existence of weak attractive and repulsive forces among the molecules of a gas and attributed to them observed deviations from the ideal gas law: $PV = nRT$. Although his contribution to the elucidation of these forces was confined to correcting the gas law through empirically determined constants, his ideas spurred others on to the investigation of their nature.

Unlike covalent bonding, which is effective at small internuclear distances and is associated with electron overlap and exchange and consequently higher energies, van der Waals bonding may operate at distances where there is little or no overlap or exchange, and is generally associated with smaller energies. For example, in crystalline iodine the structural units are known to be covalent I_2 molecules with interatomic distances about 2.7 Å, approximately that of gaseous I_2. These units are held together by van der Waals forces operating through intermolecular distances of 3.5 Å. When solid iodine is heated gently, it sublimes; yet only the van der Waals bonding is destroyed; the gaseous units are still covalent I_2 molecules.

There are at least four types of forces which contribute to the van der Waals bonding, and to get a notion of their nature, we shall examine each separately.

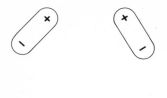

Fig. 5-9 Dipole-dipole interaction. The plus and minus signs represent the centers of positive and negative charge for the resultant molecular dipole.

The first force, attractive in type, leads to what is called the *orientation energy* and is present in molecular arrays whose constituent particles possess a permanent dipole moment, for example, HCl, NH₃, H₂O. Consider the two dipoles shown in Fig. 5-9. Obviously their electrostatic interaction would be most attractive if they were aligned with positive end to negative end, as shown in the second part of the diagram. This desire of two dipoles to be perfectly oriented with respect to one another is felt at reasonably large distances, and the tugging at one dipole by another leads to the attractive *orientation*, or dipole-dipole interaction, energy. As we shall see, this contribution to the total van der Waals energy is relatively small.

The second type of attractive force is that between a molecule with a permanent dipole and a molecule (or atom) without one. For simplicity we have pictured a dipole and a large spherical atom in Fig. 5-10. If the atom is polarizable, its electron cloud may distort toward the positive end of the dipole molecule, so that the centers of positive and negative charge in the atom no longer coincide, and an *induced* atomic dipole is

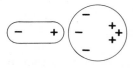

Fig. 5-10 Dipole-induced dipole interaction.

formed. The attractive interaction between the permanent dipole and the induced dipole leads to the second contribution to van der Waals binding, dubbed the *induction energy*, also a relatively small contribution.

Both the orientation energy and the induction energy can be adequately explained by classical physics. However, neither quantitatively accounts for the total van der Waals attraction in many compounds, and in particular neither accounts for the attractive forces believed to be responsible for the trend in boiling points of the rare gases, none of which possesses a permanent dipole moment. These boiling points are listed in Table 5-3.

Table 5-3   Boiling Points of Rare Gases in Degrees Kelvin

He	4.2	Kr	121
Ne	27	Xe	164
Ar	87	Rn	211

The third kind of attractive force, leading to the *dispersion energy*, accounts for the rare-gas behavior, and at the same time turns out to be the largest contributor to van der Waals attraction. Although the quantum-mechanical description gives a more accurate quantitative explanation, the simple picture afforded by the classicists is nice; hence we begin with that. We examine two hydrogen atoms at a sufficiently large distance from one another that their spherical clouds do not overlap appreciably. We then switch to the particle concept of the electron and consider a picture of the atom at some particular instant (Fig. 5-11). It is a so-called *instantaneous dipole*, which may induce in the neighboring H atom another instantaneous dipole, which fluctuates in phase with the first as the electrons move around the nuclei. The dispersion energy was attributed to the attraction between these two dipoles. How-

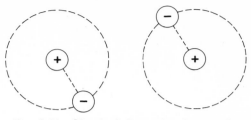

Fig. 5-11   Classical dispersion interaction.

ever, the picture provided by this theory becomes rather complicated when we try to apply it to one of the larger rare gases.

The quantum-mechanical treatment offered by London in 1930 provides more insight into dispersion forces but is considerably more complicated.   Here we say that two atoms (H atoms, for simplicity, though they are poor examples) even at distances precluding overlap "perturb" one another.   In Fig. 5-12, electron cloud I feels attracted to nucleus B, cloud II to nucleus A; clouds I and II repel one another, nuclei A and B repel.   After some mathematical manipulation (best left for graduate school) we may calculate that the net result of all these interactions is an attractive energy, small compared to that of a covalent bond (where electron clouds merge) but large compared to orientation and induction energies.

The fourth force, necessarily a large and repulsive one, becomes effective when filled electron clouds on the interacting atoms or molecules begin to overlap.   It is intimately related

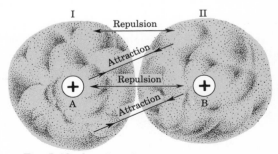

Fig. 5-12   London dispersion interaction.

to the Pauli exclusion principle and is the same force which in ionic crystals balances the electrostatic attraction at the equilibrium interionic distance.

Table 5-4 shows calculated relative magnitudes of orienta-

Table 5-4   Contributions to van der Waals Attractive Energy

Molecule	Permanent μ, D	Orientation energy	Induction energy	London dispersion energy
HI	0.38	0.35	1.68	382
HBr	0.78	6.2	4.05	176
HCl	1.03	18.6	5.4	105
NH$_3$	1.5	84	10	93
CO	0.12	0.0034	0.057	67.5

tion, induction, and London dispersion contributions to the total van der Waals attraction.   Note that orientation energies, as expected, increase as the molecular dipole moment increases. In all cases, London dispersion energies predominate, and for similar molecules (and *only* for similar molecules) increase with the number of electrons.   This latter point is one of the most important contributions of the quantum-mechanical theory.

Unlike covalent bonding, van der Waals bonding is largely nondirectional.   Packing of structural units in crystals held together by van der Waals bonds is determined primarily by geometry, and usually some variation of "closest packing" prevails.   The rare gases, for example, crystallize in hexagonal or cubic closest-packing structures for which the coordination number is 12.

5-10 THE NATURE OF THE HYDROGEN BOND

The peculiar weak bond connecting a hydrogen atom on one molecule and an electron-greedy atom on a second molecule, a *hydrogen bond,* does not easily fall into the ionic, covalent, or van der Waals categories.   Although hydrogen bonds fall in the same energy range as van der Waals interactions (less than 10 kcal/mole), they do seem to form in preferred directions, in contrast to the nondirectional van der Waals binding.   A hydrogen bond occurs between polar covalent molecules, but is itself *electrostatic* in nature.   It can be either *inter*molecular or *intra*molecular.

Some of the experimental evidence for hydrogen bonding is illustrated by the trend in boiling points of the CH_4, NH_3, H_2O, and HF families shown in Table 5-5.   Note that in this

**Table 5-5   Boiling Points in Degrees Centigrade
of Neighboring Hydride Families**

Number electrons	Methane family		Ammonia family		Water family		HF family	
10	CH_4	−164	NH_3	−33	H_2O	+100	HF	+20
18	SiH_4	−112	PH_3	−87	H_2S	−61	HCl	−85
36	GeH_4	−90	AsH_3	−55	H_2Se	−41	HBr	−67
54	SnH_4	−52	SbH_3	−18	H_2Te	−2	HI	−35

table parallel family members are isoelectronic, so that, if the intermolecular forces in the liquids were solely of the van der Waals type, we should expect similar gradual increases in boiling points within a family with increase in number of electrons. This *is* true for the methane family.

However, in the NH_3, H_2O, and HF families the parent molecules have unusually high boiling points, hinting of additional intermolecular forces in action.   These extra forces are quite characteristic of molecules containing H atoms covalently bonded to an electron-greedy atom, X in general.   In H_2O (where X = O) or in liquid HF (where X = F), atom X has the lion's share of the electron pair involved in the HX sigma bond.   If we recall a previous picture, in a polar HX bond the hydrogen atom, with a relatively small share of the electron pair, is almost a bare proton sitting on the end of the H—X sigma *MO* cloud.   The lone-pair electrons of element X on a nearby molecule bind themselves through electrostatic attraction to this highly positive proton.   The resulting "bond," in this case *inter*molecular, is a hydrogen bond.

Because of the very small size of H^+ (remember that it has *no* electrons whatsoever), it can accommodate only 2 electron-pair clouds near it at one time.   Thus the largest "coordination number" of H in a hydrogen bond is 2.

In liquid and solid HF, zigzag chainlike species occur, where the solid (shorter) lines represent covalent bonds and the dotted (longer) ones hydrogen bonds.

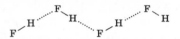

Note the linearity of the $[X—H \cdots X]$ system.   Presumably the electrostatic repulsion between the bond-pair clouds surrounding the H atom is minimized by this linear arrangement. Figure 5-13 illustrates this principle more clearly.   Water molecules are known to be tetrahedrally associated in ice, an association only partially broken down in liquid water.   The darker lobes of the sp^3 hybrids are meant to be lone pairs, the lighter lobes bond pairs.   Note the linearity of the *lp*-H-*bp* group.

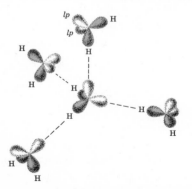

Fig. 5-13   Hydrogen bonding and tetrahedral association in water.

The extra energy needed to break these bonds when liquid water is converted to isolated gaseous water molecules is reflected in the boiling point of water. Species containing central atoms which are not particularly electron-greedy (C, S, P) do not exhibit appreciable hydrogen bonding.

*Intra*molecular hydrogen bonds are known in molecules containing neighboring —XH and —Y appendages, for example, *ortho*-iodophenol

where the dashed circle represents the delocalized π ring of the benzene framework and the dotted line shows hydrogen bonding between the —OH group (which makes benzene a phenol) and the nearby iodine atom. In this case the O-H-I system cannot be collinear and is thus associated with a weak hydrogen bond.

In nickel dimethylglyoxime (the red compound formed as a test for Ni in qualitative analysis) two of the four rings surrounding the Ni atom are closed by hydrogen bonding.

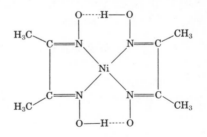

5-11 SUMMARY OF BOND TYPES

Electron-density diagrams representing the four major types of bonding—covalent, ionic, metallic, and van der Waals—are shown in Fig. 5-14. One must keep in mind that these are extreme cases and that most bonds are composites of two or more of these.

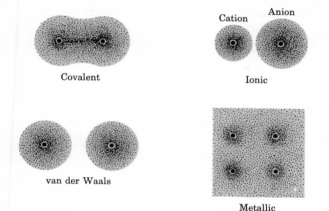

Covalent

Cation   Anion

Ionic

van der Waals

Metallic

Fig. 5-14   Electron clouds corresponding to the four major bond types.

EXERCISES

1 Compute the single-cluster stabilization energy E_{ic} and the total stabilization energy U_{ic} resulting when 1 mole of Na^+ ions and 1 mole of Cl^- ions form ion cubes of side d. Show that both results are intermediate between ion-square and lattice energies.

2 The ionization energy of Mg $(I_1 + I_2)$ is 520.8 kcal/mole. 166 kcal/mole must be *supplied* to form $O^=$ from O. Assuming an NaCl-type crystal structure, compute the stabilization energy of solid MgO relative to the isolated gaseous atoms.

3 The correction to the electrostatic model for the lattice energy of NaCl due to repulsion of electron clouds on neighboring ions takes the form

$$E_{rep} = \frac{NA_M}{n} E_{ip}$$

where n is a parameter evaluated from measurements of the compressibility of the solid. For NaCl, $n = 9.1$. Compute this correction to the lattice energy given in Fig. 5-1. The experimental lattice energy for a mole of NaCl is 181 kcal.

4 Within the following groups choose the most ionic and the least ionic compounds:

(a) $BiCl_3$, $ScCl_3$, $BeCl_2$, $AlCl_3$.
(b) TiO_2, CeO_2, SiO_2.

5 Predict the formula and shape of the complex ion of chromium and sulfur $[CrS_m]^{(2m-6)-}$.

6 Predict the coordination number of Ce^{4+} in CeO_2; Ca^{++} in CaF_2; Ti^{4+} in TiO_2.

7 Germanium metal is an intrinsic semiconductor and may also form "impurity" semiconductors. Suggest some specific impurities which may cause germanium to behave as an n-type or a p-type semiconductor.

8 Explain why the boiling points of the rare gases (Table 5-3) increase with increase in atom size.

9 KF reacts with HF to form a solid of formula KHF_2. Discuss the probable geometry and bonding in the HF_2^- ion.

10 Discuss the probable relative extent of hydrogen bonding in CH_4, CH_3OH, CH_3F, CH_3NH_2.

11 Pure liquid acetic acid ($CH_3\overset{\overset{O}{\parallel}}{C}OH$) consists of ringlike molecules of two formula units united by hydrogen bonds.

Each unit is called a dimer.   Make a drawing showing a possible structure of the dimer.

12 One might think that two possible types of sideways branching could occur in liquid HF, i.e.,

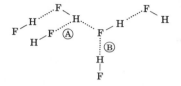

Discuss the relative probability of types A and B.

13 The density of liquid water is considerably greater than that of solid water; i.e., ice floats on water.   Suggest an explanation in terms of hydrogen bonding and structure.

REFERENCES

1 C. A. Coulson, "Valence," 2d ed., chaps. 12, 13, Oxford University Press, Fair Lawn, N.J., 1961.

2 L. Pauling, "The Nature of the Chemical Bond," 3d ed., chaps. 11–13, Cornell University Press, Ithaca, N.Y., 1960.

3 W. Moore, "Physical Chemistry," 3d ed., chap. 16, Prentice-Hall, Inc., Englewood Cliffs, N.J., 1962.

4 A. R. von Hippel, Molecular Designing of Materials, *Science*, **138**, 91 (1962).

5 R. A. Lefever, An Introduction to the Electron Theory of Metals, *J. Chem. Educ.*, **30**, 486 (1953).

6 R. A. Lefever, A Summary of Semiconductor and Transistor Theory, *J. Chem. Educ.*, **30**, 554 (1953).

7 W. G. Gehman, Standard Ionic Crystal Structures, *J. Chem. Educ.*, **40**, 53 (1963).

8 R. J. Sime, Some Models of Close Packing, *J. Chem. Educ.*, **40**, 61 (1963).

9 A. Holden and P. Singer, "Crystals and Crystal Growing," Doubleday Anchor Books, Garden City, N.Y., 1960.

STRUCTURE OF
TRANSITION-METAL
COMPOUNDS

6

6-1 INTRODUCTION

Chemists have long been fascinated by the transition metals, and for good reason: their compounds abound with intriguing magnetic properties, colors, and geometries. For example, consider the wide variety of color exhibited by just the transition-metal oxides: purple Ti_2O_3, bronze TiO, yellow V_2O_5, blue VO_2, red CrO_3, emerald green Cr_2O_3, brick red Fe_2O_3, pale green NiO, and olive MnO. Oxides of most nontransition metals are an unexciting black or white.

Since the early formulation of the orbital theory of atoms and ions, the d electrons on the transition metals have been considered responsible for these unusual properties; but it is only during the past decade that a rather specialized version of orbital theory, called crystal field theory, has very neatly correlated electronic structure, color, geometry, magnetic effects, and many other physical and chemical properties of transition-metal compounds. Crystal field theory has proved to be one of the most profitable applications of wave mechanics to chemical problems.

Before discussing crystal field theory itself, we digress briefly to consider the measurement and structural significance of color and the magnetic properties of matter.

6-2 COLOR

In Chap. 1 we learned that light in its particle nature consists of photons, each characterized by a wavelength or color, the wavelength being intimately related to the energy of the photon through the relationship

$$E = \frac{hc}{\lambda}$$

Only those photons whose wavelengths fall in the range 4,000 to 7,000 Å stimulate the human sense of sight, i.e., are visible. Red, the long-wavelength color, corresponds to low energy, and violet, with short wavelength, to high energy. Between these limits, with increasing energy are photons associated with the colors orange, yellow, green, and blue. Ordinary white light, such as that emitted from a hot tungsten filament, is a continuum of all colors and energies, and black corresponds to absence of visibly detectable photons.

We see an opaque object primarily by light reflected from its surface. Consequently, an object illuminated by white light may appear red in color because it is absorbing high-energy photons and reflecting the lower-energy red ones from its surface. A simplified plot showing light absorption versus energy or color of the incident photon is shown in Fig. 6-1 for a red object, along with representative *absorption spectra* of some objects of other colors.

The mechanism of absorption of light by a solid or liquid is closely related to that of emission of photons by gaseous ions excited in a flame (Chap. 2). When sodium ions in a salt or

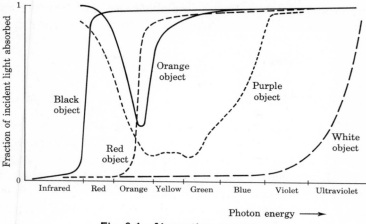

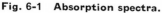

Fig. 6-1   Absorption spectra.

salt solution are vaporized in a bunsen flame, electrons on the gaseous metal ions are excited to higher energy levels and, as they return to the ground state, emit photons of energy corresponding to the color yellow. At room temperature, certain of the electrons in a solid or solution when bombarded with white light may absorb photons whose energies correspond either to allowed quantum jumps within an ion or to the energy necessary to transfer the electron from an outer orbital on one ion to an empty orbital on an ion of a different type. For example, the orange-yellow color of cadmium sulfide is probably due to electron transfer of a $3p$ electron on a sulfide ion to a vacant orbital on a nearby cadmium ion. Those photons not acceptable for the process (the lower-energy red, yellow, and orange ones) are reflected back to us as the characteristic color of the compound. The transferred or excited electron usually dissipates its energy by contributing it to the vibrational motions of the ions in the solid lattice or to vibrational, rotational, and translational motions of molecules in solution. Consequently no emission process (light flash) usually occurs. Since the lifetime of the excited state is very short, the electron is soon back in its ground state ready for another absorption.

Vibrational processes are not available to isolated atoms or ions in the gas phase; hence the existence of emission spectra for these.

6-3 MAGNETIC PROPERTIES

All substances with few exceptions contain atoms with one or more filled electron levels (s^2, p^6, d^{10}, . . .).   When placed in the magnetic field existing between the poles of a natural magnet or an electromagnet, such a substance experiences a weak repulsion by the field, tending to push it away.   This phenomenon is known as *diamagnetism* and is independent of temperature (see Fig. 6-2).

In contrast, substances containing atoms with one or more unpaired electrons are strongly attracted into magnetic fields, an attraction inversely dependent on temperature.   This phenomenon is known as *paramagnetism*.   The forces associated with paramagnetism are considerably larger than those of diamagnetism and usually mask them almost completely.   An atom with several completed levels and only one unpaired electron is still strongly paramagnetic.

The property known as *ferromagnetism* is rare, exhibited only by iron metal and several other substances which are attracted into magnetic fields by forces thousands of times larger than paramagnetic ones.

Though the theory of ferromagnetism is complex, we can

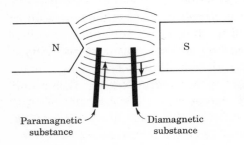

Paramagnetic
substance

Diamagnetic
substance

Fig. 6-2   Behavior of paramagnetic and diamagnetic substances in a magnetic field.

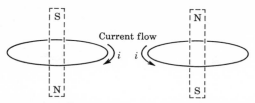

Fig. 6-3   Bar magnet representation of the magnetic field induced by a flow of current through a loop.

get a qualitative picture of the causes of diamagnetism and paramagnetism through a simple model based on the laws of classical physics.   When an electric current (a flow of negative charge) is passed through a circular loop such as that of Fig. 6-3, a magnetic field is induced perpendicular to the loop, with a north and south pole (like a little bar magnet) dependent upon the direction of electron flow.   An electron undergoing orbital motion (think for a moment of a Bohr orbit) or spinning around its axis in an α or β way is a negative charge undergoing angular motion (though the loop in spin motion has zero radius), and as a result both spin and orbital motion have intrinsic magnetic fields associated with them.   When two electrons are spin-paired, the magnetic fields are in opposite directions and cancel. When an atom or molecule has one or more *unpaired* electrons, it has a permanent resultant magnetic field associated with it, which in a sense causes it to act like a little bar magnet.   When placed in an external magnetic field, the bar magnet will be attracted by forces tending to line up its poles with the poles of the field (north to south) in so much as temperature permits. Increasing temperature increases the translational motion of the bar magnets and makes alignment more difficult.   Thus paramagnetic forces seem to decrease with increasing temperature.

When electrons are part of a closed orbital level, not only their spin magnetic fields but also the fields associated with their orbital motion cancel (are "coupled").   When brought into the presence of an external field, the orbital "bar magnets" are uncoupled slightly, producing a resultant magnetic field which always *opposes* the direction of the external field, whatever it may be. In other words, if the diamagnetic substance is approaching the north pole of an external magnetic field, a resultant bar magnet with its north pole pointed at the field is created by uncoupling the orbital bar magnets. This is a repulsive situation, because like poles repel, and the substance is pushed from the field. Unlike paramagnetism, diamagnetism is independent of temperature, because here there is no question of lining up rapidly moving molecules; the opposing magnetic field is created by the electrons no matter in which direction they approach the external field.

More details about these processes may be found in Halliday and Resnick (2).

An apparatus for measuring these effects, the Gouy balance, is illustrated in Fig. 6-4. The sample to be studied, S, is hung from one arm of a sensitive analytical balance, so that it is hovering at the edge of the magnetic field produced between the poles of an electromagnet P. With the magnet turned off, the weight of the sample is balanced with known weights added to pan A. Then the electromagnet is turned on, producing a field of known strength, and the sample, if paramagnetic, undergoes an apparent increase in weight due to the pull of the field,

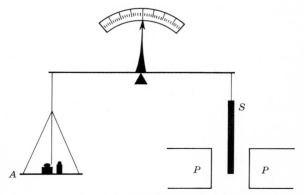

Fig. 6-4   The Gouy balance.

or, if diamagnetic, a decrease in weight due to repulsion by the field. These weight changes can be measured by adding or removing weights from the pan A until the balance pointer is again zeroed. Along with data on sample weight, composition, and temperature, these weight changes are used to compute a quantity called the magnetic dipole moment μ, analogous to the electric dipole moment described in Chap. 4. Usually μ is expressed as a multiple of a unit called the Bohr magneton (BM). For an atom or molecule with n unpaired electrons the magnitude of μ is $[n(n + 2)]^{1/2}$. We shall have occasion later to compute n from the measured magnetic dipole moments of transition-metal ions.

6-4 FUNDAMENTALS OF CRYSTAL FIELD THEORY

There are many excited energy levels available to electrons in isolated gaseous transition-metal ions, and the positions of these relative to the ground states are quite well known through careful study of emission spectra. Nevertheless these are not adequate to explain the absorption energies associated with the colors of transition-metal compounds. Any respectable theory of their structure must remedy this and must also be compatible with experimentally observed changes in color and magnetic properties with change in oxidation number and environment of the metal ion. Crystal field theory has succeeded in these and many other respects, and, fortunately, to understand its basic principles, we need accept only two things: the shapes of the $3d$ orbitals, as shown in Fig. 6-5, and the simple law of electrostatics that says like charges repel one another.

We may best explain the theory by considering an example, the perturbation of the $Ti^{3+}(3d^1)$ ion in an oxide lattice. We recall that in the isolated ion the single d electron has no preference as to which d orbital it will occupy, all five being degenerate with respect to energy and thus equally stable. Arbitrarily we put it in the central orbital in the energy-level

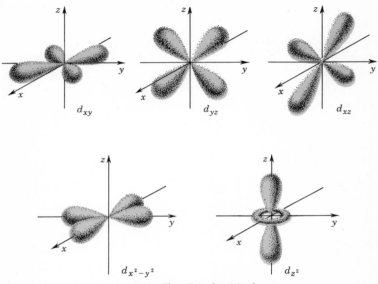

Fig. 6-5   The five d orbitals.

diagram in Fig. 6-6.   We then imagine a situation wherein 12
electrons in their cloudlike character are taken from some external pot of electrons and shaped into a spherical shell surrounding the Ti^{3+} ion at some known radius R, as illustrated in

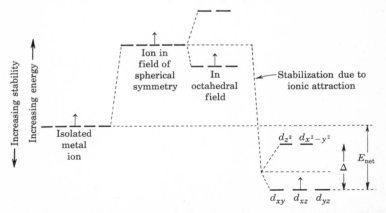

Fig. 6-6   Crystal field energy relationships for an octahedral system.

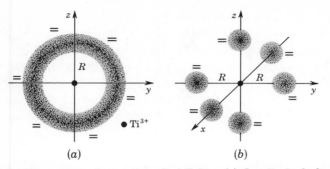

(a) (b)

Fig. 6-7 Formation of an octahedral field. (a) **A spherical electron cloud surrounding the metal ion;** (b) **redistribution of charges to octahedral symmetry.**

cross section in Fig. 6-7a. The single d electron on Ti^{3+} will find each orbital equally uncomfortable because of the spherical symmetry of the repulsive cloud. In terms of energy the system is less stable than the isolated ion (so far as the electron is concerned), but the orbital degeneracy is retained, as shown in Fig. 6-6. To bring our model closer to the real physical situation (six oxide ions arranged octahedrally around the Ti^{3+}), we conceive of another process, in which the spherical cloud is rearranged so that two electrons are concentrated in very small volumes at distances $\pm R$ along each of the three coordinate axes in space (Fig. 6-7b). The single d electron now finds the d_{z^2} and the $d_{x^2-y^2}$ orbitals, with their lobes pointing directly at the clouds along the axes, electrostatically less comfortable than in the spherically symmetric case, and the d_{xy}, d_{xz}, and d_{yz} orbitals, with lobes pointing into empty space between the axes, considerably more comfortable. The d orbitals are no longer degenerate with respect to energy, and in fact are split into the two levels shown in Fig. 6-6. It is not obvious from the pictures that the d_{z^2} orbital is equivalent to $d_{x^2-y^2}$ in this environment, but wave-mechanical arguments (which we can only accept in this text) establish that it is so. These treatments also show that, if the total energy difference between the upper and lower levels is designated Δ (Fig. 6-6), then the increase in stability and the decrease in stability over the spherically symmetric case are $\frac{2}{5}\Delta$ and $\frac{3}{5}\Delta$, respectively. This is simply a statement of energy balance: in our rearrangement of the electron cloud the number of orbitals (3) which increased in stability multiplied by the increase $\frac{2}{5}\Delta$ equals the number of orbitals (2) which decreased in stability times the decrease $\frac{3}{5}\Delta$. This rule will always hold, whatever the splitting diagram.

We may now identify the six doubly negative electron clouds surrounding the Ti^{3+} ion with six $O^=$ ions in a crystal lattice of Ti_2O_3. Here the six $O^=$ are located around the Ti^{3+} in an arrangement closely approximating perfect octahedral symmetry. In this field the Ti^{3+} ion gains a *crystal field stabilization energy (CFSE)* of $\frac{2}{5}\Delta$, which we should not expect without knowledge of the shapes of d orbitals! The *CFSE*, as defined, is the difference between a hypothetical situation (where the oxide electrons are smeared into a spherical shell) and a real one (where they are localized near the oxygen nuclei), and is thus clearly not a directly measurable quantity. Nevertheless, as we shall see, the existence of crystal field stabilization energy (proved indirectly) strongly influences the properties of transition-metal compounds.

Before proceeding further, we must point out that the crystal field stabilization energy is a relatively small energy superimposed on the larger electrostatic energies present in an ionic crystal. To get the complete picture, we must recognize that besides the electronic repulsion energies described thus far the Ti^{3+} ion as a whole feels a strong electrostatic attraction for the six negative oxide ions. This is so large that, when it is combined with the electronic repulsion, the net energy of the system is lower than that of the isolated ions. This net energy is related to the classical crystal lattice energy U_L of Chap. 5 and is responsible for the stability of the crystal. The crystal field stabilization energy is a small contribution to this (see Fig. 6-6).

6-5 EXPLANATION AND USE OF ABSORPTION SPECTRA

We may immediately suggest an explanation for the color of Ti_2O_3. The absorption spectrum of the solid indicates a transition occurring in the vicinity of 2.5 ev. A study of the emission spectrum of isolated Ti^{3+} ions yields no electronic change which can be identified with this number. If we associate this energy with an electron jump in the presence of the crystal field from the lower d orbitals to one of the higher ones (Fig. 6-6), we can see that the splitting parameter Δ_{oct} for Ti^{3+} must have a value 2.5 ev. Later we shall show that the Δ values obtained in this way are consistent with other experimental values, which indicates that the transition identification is correct.

Absorption spectra thus provide powerful tools for obtaining the Δ parameters and, through the energy-balance relationship, the crystal field stabilization energy. For Ti^{3+}, for example, if Δ is 2.5 ev, then the *CFSE*, being $\frac{2}{5}\Delta$, is 1.0 ev. Table 6-1 contains the Δ values gleaned from spectral studies

Table 6-1 Some Properties of Doubly Positive Transition-metal Ions

Ion	Configuration	Theoretical μ for isolated ion, BM	*CFSE* in weak octahedral field	*CFSE* in strong octahedral field	Spectroscopic Δ values for hexahydrated ions, ev
Ca^{2+}	$(Ar\ core)^{18}\ 3d^0$	0	0	0	
Sc^{2+}	$(Ar\ core)^{18}\ 3d^1$	1.73	$\frac{2}{5}\Delta$	$\frac{2}{5}\Delta$	
Ti^{2+}	$(Ar\ core)^{18}\ 3d^2$	2.83	$\frac{4}{5}\Delta$	$\frac{4}{5}\Delta$	
V^{2+}	$(Ar\ core)^{18}\ 3d^3$	3.87	$\frac{6}{5}\Delta$	$\frac{6}{5}\Delta$	1.56
Cr^{2+}	$(Ar\ core)^{18}\ 3d^4$	4.90	$\frac{3}{5}\Delta$	$\frac{8}{5}\Delta - W$	1.72
Mn^{2+}	$(Ar\ core)^{18}\ 3d^5$	5.92	0	$\frac{10}{5}\Delta - W'$	0.97
Fe^{2+}	$(Ar\ core)^{18}\ 3d^6$	4.90	$\frac{2}{5}\Delta$	$\frac{12}{5}\Delta - W''$	1.29
Co^{2+}	$(Ar\ core)^{18}\ 3d^7$	3.87	$\frac{4}{5}\Delta$	$\frac{9}{5}\Delta - W'''$	1.15
Ni^{2+}	$(Ar\ core)^{18}\ 3d^8$	2.83	$\frac{6}{5}\Delta$	$\frac{6}{5}\Delta$	1.05
Cu^{2+}	$(Ar\ core)^{18}\ 3d^9$	1.73	$\frac{3}{5}\Delta$	$\frac{3}{5}\Delta$	1.56
Zn^{2+}	$(Ar\ core)^{18}\ 3d^{10}$	0	0	0	

of many of the doubly positive, hexahydrated transition-metal ions in solution. In these systems the perturbing elements are the lone-pair electrons on the water molecules, arranged octahedrally around the metal ion. We shall use the numbers of Table 6-1 in Sec. 6-9 to explain the heats of hydration of these molecules.

6-6 NONOCTAHEDRAL SYSTEMS

Certainly not all transition-metal ions are surrounded by anions or molecules in octahedral symmetry in their compounds. Other common geometries are square planar, tetrahedral, trigonal, tetragonal, and linear, and each arrangement of perturbing agents (called ligands) produces its own distinctive splitting pattern. We illustrate some of these in Fig. 6-8.

Tetrahedral symmetry is closely related to octahedral symmetry. Figure 6-8a shows how one may construct a tetrahedron by placing ligands on four appropriate corners of a cube. In this diagram the x and y axes emerge from the sides of the cube and the z axis from the center of the top face. The tiny black squares show the relative positions of ligands in octahedral symmetry, with metal-ligand distances the same as those in the tetrahedron. Note that the tetrahedral ligands avoid the density lobes of the d_{z^2} and $d_{x^2-y^2}$ orbitals and are more likely to perturb the other three d orbitals. It is not very surprising then to learn that the splitting pattern is inverted when octahedral is replaced by tetrahedral symmetry, although admittedly it does not seem possible to guess this from the pictures. Here we must simply accept the results of

Fig. 6-8   Fields of symmetry other than octahedral. (a) **A tetrahedral array of ligands (black circles) with respect to an octahedral array (squares) and the associated splitting diagrams;** (b) **octahedral, tetragonal, and square planar arrays and their splitting diagrams;** (c) **a trigonal array of ligands and the splitting diagrams associated with changes in β from 90° to 0°.**

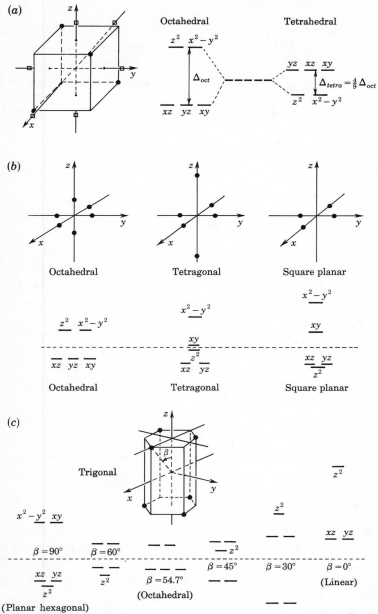

(a)

Octahedral

z^2 x^2-y^2

Δ_{oct}

xz yz xy

Tetrahedral

yz xz xy

$\Delta_{tetra}=\frac{4}{9}\Delta_{oct}$

z^2 x^2-y^2

(b)

Octahedral

Tetragonal

Square planar

x^2-y^2

z^2 x^2-y^2

xz yz xy

Octahedral

x^2-y^2

xy

z^2

xz yz

Tetragonal

x^2-y^2

xy

xz yz

z^2

Square planar

(c)

Trigonal

x^2-y^2 xy

$\beta=90°$ $\beta=60°$

xz yz

z^2

(Planar hexagonal)

z^2

$\beta=54.7°$
(Octahedral)

z^2

$\beta=45°$

$\beta=30°$

z^2

xz yz

$\beta=0°$
(Linear)

xy x^2-y^2

the more rigorous mathematical treatments. These show also that the splitting associated with tetrahedral symmetry is smaller than that of octahedral; this is logical since the number of ligands is smaller. For equivalent ligand charges and distances

$$\Delta_{tetra} = -\tfrac{4}{9}\Delta_{oct}$$

where the minus sign means reversal of orbital levels.

Figure 6-8b illustrates the changes which occur in splitting pattern when, starting with a perfect octahedron, one stretches the ligand-metal distances along the z axis, to form a system of *tetragonal* symmetry, and then removes them completely, leaving the metal ion in a *square planar* field.

Trigonal symmetry is obtained when one starts with a perfect octahedron, redefines the position of the x, y, and z axes, as shown in Fig. 6-8c, and either compresses or stretches the solid figure along the z axis, retaining the ligand-metal distances and keeping the planes of the upper and lower triangles parallel. For a perfect octahedron the angle β is 54.7°; for compression, β is larger; for stretching, β is smaller.   The extreme case where $\beta = 0$ corresponds to a field of *linear* symmetry; when $\beta = 90°$, all ligands lie in the xy plane forming a perfect *hexagonal planar* field around the metal.

Some of these fancier splitting diagrams are employed in the exercises at the end of the chapter.

6-7   SYSTEMS WITH MORE THAN ONE d ELECTRON; STRONG AND WEAK CRYSTAL FIELDS

The general features of all the splitting diagrams discussed so far are the same when the metal ion possesses more than one d electron.   However, we must now consider the existence of interactions among the d electrons themselves and the effect of this on the crystal field stabilization energy.

We consider first the case of an ion with two d electrons

in a site of octahedral symmetry. We know now what will happen to the first d electron. The second will simply join the first in the lower energy level, as shown in Fig. 6-9, occupying a separate orbital in accordance with Hund's rule, and the system will attain a total $CFSE$ of $2(\frac{2}{5}\Delta)$, or $\frac{4}{5}\Delta$. Since the spin configuration is the same as that of the isolated ion, there will be no significant energy effects due to changes in d electron interactions. A third d electron should behave similarly and increase the crystal field stabilization energy by $\frac{2}{5}\Delta$ more.

A fourth d electron, however, is faced with a difficult decision: it may go down to the lower energy level and pair with one of the repulsive electrons already there, or it may go to the higher, less stable energy level and remain unpaired. If it goes down, the stability of the system increases by $\frac{2}{5}\Delta$ *minus* the interaction energy or work W which must be expended when the electrons pair. If the electron goes to the higher level, the very stable isolated-ion spin configuration is retained (nothing is lost due to electron interaction), but $\frac{3}{5}\Delta$ is subtracted from the $CFSE$ of the system. The decision of the fourth electron (and the fifth and the sixth) is determined by the magnitude of the splitting parameter Δ (the so-called crystal field *strength*) relative to the work of pairing. Two extreme cases can be distinguished, and many, but not all, transition-metal systems fall into one of them. In general, if Δ is very large (if the field is strong), electrons will tend to pair in the lower level at the expense of the associated repulsion energies and form what are called *low-spin* configurations. If the field is very weak (if Δ is small), then the d electrons will retain their maximum-spin configuration, the *high-spin* case, and sacrifice $CFSE$ in so doing. More specifically, for the d^4 case, if $\frac{3}{5}\Delta$ is greater than $\frac{8}{5}\Delta - W$, then the high-spin configuration will be favored. If the reverse of the inequality is true, then the low-spin configuration will be favored.

Strong- and weak-field distributions for all d^n configurations are shown in Fig. 6-9. Note that for strong fields the electrons always pair in the lower level first, filling it before

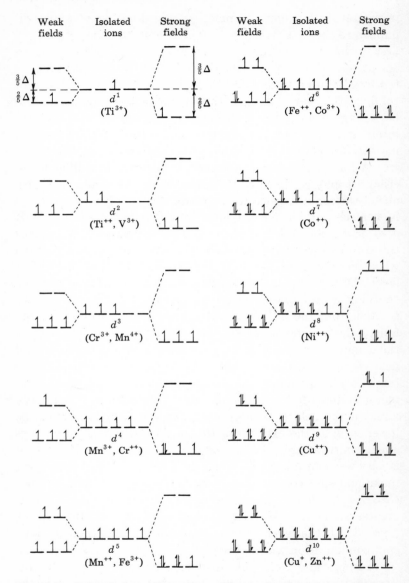

Fig. 6-9 d-electron configurations for weak and strong fields of octahedral symmetry.

entering the higher level.   For weak fields each orbital, whether of high or low energy, receives one electron before any pairing starts.   Weak-field configurations always have the same pairing scheme as the free ions.

6-8 FACTORS INFLUENCING FIELD STRENGTH

The strength of the field around an ion depends largely upon the ligand, its size and shape and distance from the metal ion. From studies of absorption spectra it is possible to arrange many common ligands in what is called the *spectrochemical series*, a portion of which, indicating increasing splitting power of the ligand, is:

$$I^- < Br^- < Cl^- < F^- < H_2O \cong O^= < NH_3 \lll CN^-$$

Thus the complex ion $FeF_6{}^{3-}$ with the weaker ligand F^- exists in a high-spin configuration, as shown by measurements of its magnetic dipole moment. μ is approximately 6 BM, consistent with the presence of five unpaired electrons in a weak octahedral field.   On the other hand, the ion $Fe(CN)_6{}^{3-}$, of similar geometry, has a μ of approximately 1.7 BM, consistent with a low-spin configuration and one unpaired electron.   The strong field of the CN^- ion causes maximum pairing of the five Fe^{3+} d electrons in the lower energy level.   This example incidentally shows how crystal field theory explains the once perplexing variation in magnetic properties of the same metal ion in different compounds.

The splitting power of a particular ligand is determined by how closely the perturbing negative electrons approach the d orbitals on the transition-metal ion.   This in turn depends upon the size of the ligand and its polarizability.   Large unwieldy ligands cannot approach the metal ion as closely as smaller ones; they "elbow" one another out.   This combined with their lower charge-to-volume ratio (ionic potential) makes them less effective perturbing agents.

Under the attractive field exerted by the positively charged metal cation, the electron clouds on certain ligands may be distorted toward the metal, thus increasing the perturbation of the d electrons. Highly electronegative (electron-greedy) ligands resist distortion (polarization) and would be expected to be weaker in splitting power.

Despite these rationalizations the power of a ligand cannot always be predicted satisfactorily. We would expect, on the basis of size and ionic potential, that I^-, relative to F^-, should be the weaker ligand. However, since F is more electronegative, we would expect that I^- should be more polarizable and consequently the stronger ligand. Experimental results indicate that I^- is weaker, and the main conclusion we can draw from this is that here, as in all of chemistry, the court of last appeal is the experiment.

6-9 EXPLANATION OF THE STRANGE DOUBLE-HUMPED CURVES

One of the biggest accomplishments of crystal field theory is the satisfactory explanation of the twin peaks observed when

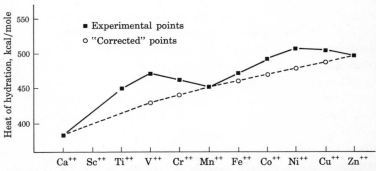

Fig. 6-10   **Experimental and "corrected" heats of hydration of doubly positive transition-metal ions.**

many physical properties of transition metals are plotted versus atomic number. Figure 6-10 illustrates such a variation in the heats of hydration of the doubly positive ions. The heat of hydration, E_h, is the total increase in stability experienced by the isolated ion when it becomes surrounded by about six water molecules in solution, i.e.,

$$Tr^{++} + 6H_2O \rightarrow Tr(H_2O)_6{}^{++} + E_h$$

E_h is the energy which must be supplied to the complex ion to reverse the hydration process (in theory). If we were unaware of crystal field effects we would expect this energy to increase slowly and smoothly from Ca^{++} to Zn^{++} due to the ligands' attraction for the increasing effective charge on the metal ion. Although all ions in the series are formally doubly positive species, their *effective* charges are not $+2$. From Ca^{++} to Zn^{++} the nuclear charges increase regularly; yet each increase is only partially canceled by the increase in the number of d electrons externally. d electrons are relatively poor shielders.

The experimental curve of hydration energies, however, shows two distinct peaks, with a minimum occurring at Mn^{++}. If we subtract from this curve the crystal field stabilization energies of doubly positive ions in a weak field (using stabilization-energy expressions and Δ values of Table 6-1, appropriately converted to kilocalories per mole), the result is the relatively smooth curve expected from our arguments above. The double-humped character of the curve is simply due to the extra stability attained by the d electrons in an octahedral field.

Similar curves showing trends in ionic radii, lattice energies, dissociation energies of gaseous molecules, stability constants of complex ions, and even reaction rates on the surfaces of transition-metal compounds have been beautifully explained by crystal field theory. Descriptions of some of these may be found in the references at the chapter end, while others are developed in the exercise section.

6-10 THE SPINEL CRYSTAL STRUCTURES

Crystal field theory brought some measure of order into the theory of the complex metal oxide systems called *spinels*. These have the general formula $M^{2+}M_2^{3+}O_4$, where M may be Mn, Fe, Co, or many other transition or nontransition metal ions. M^{2+} and M^{3+} may represent two different metals or may be the same metal in two different oxidation states.   For example, the oxides Fe_3O_4 and Mn_3O_4 are spinels, whose formulas may be more explicitly written $Fe^{2+}Fe_2^{3+}O_4$ and $Mn^{2+}Mn_2^{3+}O_4$.

The spinel lattices contain two different types of sites for the metal ions: one-third of the total metal sites are surrounded by a tetrahedron of oxide ions; two-thirds by octahedrally located oxide ions.   Two extreme cases of spinels are distinguished: a *normal* spinel with all M^{2+} ions at tetrahedral sites and all M^{3+} ions at octahedral sites (the formula allows this); and an *inverted* spinel with M^{3+} ions occupying all tetrahedral sites and half of the octahedral sites, while M^{2+} ions take all remaining octahedral sites.

With this in mind, let us now ask why the oxide Mn_3O_4 is a normal spinel, while Fe_3O_4 is inverted.   We assume that oxide ions, like water molecules, produce a weak field.   The answer then is rather simple: while $Mn^{2+}(d^5)$ and $Fe^{3+}(d^5)$ in weak fields gain no net *CFSE* in either tetrahedral or octahedral sites, the $Mn^{3+}(d^4)$ and $Fe^{2+}(d^6)$ ions both do.   Since for equivalent distances and ligands Δ_{oct} is larger than Δ_{tetra}, the d^4 and d^6 ions will preferentially occupy the octahedral sites, maximizing the *CFSE* of the system.   Hence for Mn_3O_4, all $Mn^{3+}(d^4)$ ions are in octahedral sites, with all $Mn^{2+}(d^5)$ in tetrahedral sites (a normal spinel).   For Fe_3O_4, all $Fe^{2+}(d^6)$ ions are in octahedral sites, but since there are not enough Fe^{2+} ions to occupy all of them, the remaining octahedral and tetrahedral sites are held by Fe^{3+} ions (an inverted spinel).

While the theory and experimental data tie together very neatly for the above example and several other systems, unfortunately this is not always true.   Frequently spinels do not fall into the clear-cut categories, normal or inverted, but are mixed, indicating a very complicated interplay of forces rather than the simple analysis described above.   Current research on spinels and related structures is very active.

6-11 DISTORTION AND THE JAHN-TELLER THEOREM

Hand in hand with a general quantum-mechanical rule known as the Jahn-Teller theorem, crystal field theory led the way to the explanation of why certain six-coordinated transition-metal compounds were distorted from perfect octahedral symmetry. In a simplified form, the Jahn-Teller theorem states that nature dislikes orbitally degenerate ground states and will distort the system in such a way as to render them nondegenerate.   An example of an orbitally degenerate ground state is the d^1 configuration in an octahedral field; such a system has threefold orbital degeneracy, for there are three ways we can distribute the electron among the lower orbitals with the same energy. The d^2 configuration (with unpaired electrons) also has threefold orbital degeneracy.   A d^3 configuration, however, in the same environment is nondegenerate.   (Remember that *electrons* are indistinguishable, while the names d_{xy}, d_{xz}, d_{yz} imply that we can tell the *orbitals* apart.)

A great deal of evidence on Jahn-Teller distortions has been gathered for compounds containing Cu^{2+} ion.   Its d^9 configuration has in either strong or weak octahedral fields a twofold orbital degeneracy in the upper energy level.   The two possible configurations are: I, $(d_{x^2-y^2})^2(d_{z^2})^1$ and II, $(d_{x^2-y^2})^1(d_{z^2})^2$.   In distribution I the two ligands along the z axis are less shielded from the metal nuclear charge and consequently may be attracted closer, resulting in a distorted octahedron with two short and four long metal-ligand distances.   As the ligands move in, they perturb the d_{z^2} electron more, making this level less stable than the $d_{x^2-y^2}$.   The resulting splitting pattern is

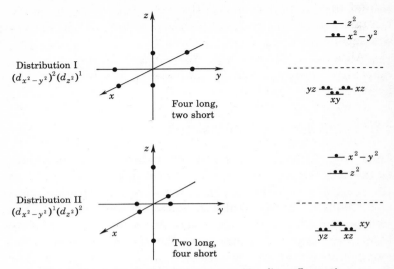

Fig. 6-11   Jahn-Teller distortion in the d^9 configuration.

shown in Fig. 6-11. Note that in the distorted structure the orbital degeneracy is removed, and a secondary smaller effect is apparent in the lower-energy orbitals. For distribution II, the four ligands in the xy plane move in, resulting in four short and two long metal-ligand distances and the splitting diagram shown. Unfortunately there is no sure way of predicting which of the two distortions will occur, and we must again appeal to experiment to tell us. Cu^{2+} systems prefer the "4 short, 2 long" distortion.

Some other examples of Jahn-Teller distortions are hidden among the exercises at the end of the chapter. There are many such distortions known in transition-metal chemistry, and until the development of crystal field theory, they were unexplained.

6-12   EFFECTS OF COVALENCE

Although so far we have described transition-metal systems in terms of a completely ionic model, i.e., with electrons localized around their respective nuclei, there is a large body of experimental evidence indicating that delocalization of electrons and consequent partial covalence does occur.

Although the ionic model explains the bulk features of the absorption spectra of many transition-metal compounds, experimental and theoretical results do not often agree exactly. In many compounds the actual metal-ligand distances are much smaller than the sum of ionic radii. Lattice energies computed for many of the salts and oxides of transition metals (even with elaborate corrections) are quite different from experimental values. All these differences may be attributed to the effect of covalence, i.e., smearing or delocalization of electron clouds between metal and ligands. The idea of partial covalence in these compounds is not surprising, for by now we know that few systems belong to the extreme classifications: purely ionic and purely covalent.

The molecular-orbital theory of transition-metal compounds takes into account the mixing of ligand and metal electron clouds and is consequently favored over the ionic model by many chemists. Molecular-orbital *calculations*, however, have proved no more successful in quantitative explanation of properties of transition-metal compounds than those based on the ionic model.

To build molecular orbitals for an octahedral complex, generally one assumes that six σ bonds may form by overlap of ligand orbitals with metal orbitals directed along the x, y, and z axes: $4s$, $4p_x$, $4p_y$, $4p_z$, $3d_{z^2}$, $3d_{x^2-y^2}$. The $3d_{xy}$, $3d_{xz}$, and $3d_{yz}$ orbitals may be assumed *nonbonding* or in some systems may be used to form π *MO*'s by sideways overlap with ligand p orbitals.

Figure 6-12 illustrates a molecular-orbital energy diagram for an octahedral complex, where for simplicity only σ *MO*'s are considered. The six ligand and six metal orbitals smear together to form six partially degenerate *bonding* molecular orbitals (whose levels are labeled σ_1, σ_2, and σ_3) and six *antibonding MO*'s (with levels labeled σ_1^*, σ_2^*, and σ_3^*). Electrons

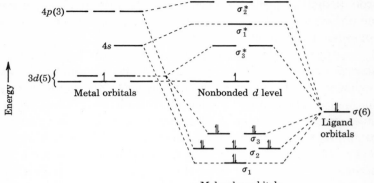

Fig. 6-12   Molecular-orbital energy diagram for the octahedral complex ion Ti(H₂O)₆³⁺. The numbers in parentheses represent degeneracies. Dotted lines indicate the metal and ligand orbitals mixed to build the *MO*'s.

from both metal and ligands occupy these MO's. In the $Ti(H_2O)_6{}^{3+}$ complex ion, for example, one lone pair on each of the six water molecules contributes to the σ bond formation, filling the lowest six molecular orbitals in Fig. 6-12.   The nonbonding d level contains the $Ti^{3+}(d^1)$ electron.   The absorption spectrum of $Ti(H_2O)_6{}^{3+}$ is now attributed to a transition from this triply degenerate ground state to the doubly degenerate σ_3^* level, composed partly of $d_{x^2-y^2}$ and d_{z^2} orbitals, an identification differing from that of the ionic model only in that here the d orbitals involved are not "pure."

The amount of ligand-metal electron mixing necessarily varies from compound to compound.   We may formulate some general rules about the degree of covalence to be expected, basing our arguments on the concept of ionic potential (Chap. 5).   For similar compounds, FeO, MnO, CoO, NiO, we expect covalence to increase with decrease in metal-ion size.   For series like TiO_2, V_2O_5, CrO_3, Mn_2O_7, we expect increasing covalence with increase in oxidation number of the metal.   As the ligand polarizability increases, covalence should increase. The CN⁻ ion, for example, is easily distorted, and in the complex ion $Fe(CN)_6^{3-}$ the ligand orbitals overlap strongly with metal orbitals. As a result, the energies of the molecular orbitals involving the $d_{x^2-y^2}$ and d_{z^2} orbitals (σ_3 and σ_3^*) become respectively highly stable and unstable with respect to the nonbonding d level, and the Fe^{3+} d electrons pair in a *low-spin* configuration in the nonbonding d level after 12 CN^- lone-pair electrons have filled σ_1, σ_2, and σ_3 levels (Fig. 6-13a). In contrast, in the ion FeF_6^{3-} the F^- electron pairs are not easily distorted toward the metal and overlap is smaller. The *MO*'s likely to form do not differ appreciably in energy from the isolated *AO*'s; i.e., there is less stabilization due to mixing of electron clouds (Fig. 6-13b), and the outer electrons occupy the nonbonding d level and the nearby σ_3^* level in a *high-spin* configuration. Roughly correlating the two models, we may say that strong-field complexes (within the ionic model) correspond to highly covalent systems (within the *MO* treatment), while the weak-field complexes are only slightly covalent.

Perhaps more quantitative things may be said about the

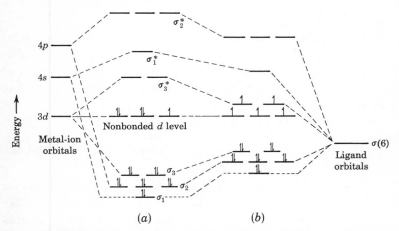

Fig. 6-13   Molecular-orbital energy diagrams for complex ions of Fe^{3+}.
(a) **Covalent, low-spin $Fe(CN)_6^{3-}$, for which** *MO* **energies are considerably different from those of the separated ions;** (b) **the "ionic," high-spin FeF_6^{3-}, for which** *MO* **energies differ only slightly from energies of separated ions.**

degree of covalence in the compounds when rigorous calculations, yielding accurate descriptions of electron density distributions, have been performed. Since such calculations on many-electron *atoms* have not yet yielded results in complete agreement with experiment, this may be some time in the future!

EXERCISES

1 The $Ti(H_2O)_6{}^{3+}$ complex ion shows a strong absorption at 20,400 cm^{-1}. (*a*) Predict whether $Ti(NH_3)_6{}^{3+}$ would absorb light of a higher or lower energy. (*b*) Would PH_3 as a ligand move the absorption peak to higher or lower energy relative to NH_3? (N is more electron-greedy than P.)

2 Consider each of the species Cr^0, Cr^{2+}, and Cr^{3+} in an octahedral field. (*a*) Use a suitable diagram to represent the occupation of energy levels for weak and strong fields around the metal or its ions. (*b*) Explain how magnetic properties may be used to distinguish the strong and weak extremes for each case.

3 Taking the z axis as the internuclear axis, derive from orbital pictures the splitting diagram expected for gaseous transition-metal oxides TrO, where Tr is any transition metal of the first series. If E_D is the energy associated with the process

$$TrO + E_D \rightarrow Tr^{++} + O^= \text{ (isolated ions)}$$

sketch a plot of expected E_D versus metal ion across the series.

4 The complex ion $Ni(CN)_4{}^=$ exists in a square planar configuration. Keeping in mind the position of CN^- in the spectrochemical series, compute in Bohr magnetons the magnetic dipole moment expected for the salt $Na_2[Ni(CN)_4]\cdot 3H_2O$. (See Fig. 6-8*b* for the square planar splitting diagram.) Compute the dipole moment assuming a tetrahedral configuration of CN^- ions. Would magnetic measurements distinguish between these two forms?

5 For which d-electron configurations in an octahedral field would you expect no Jahn-Teller distortion?

6 For the d^1 configuration in a weak trigonal field would you expect β to be larger or smaller than the perfect octahedral angle? (Refer to Fig. 6-8c.) What about d^2 and d^3?

7 Explain the fact that the tetrahedron of Cl^- ions surrounding a Cu^{++} ion in the complex $CuCl_4^-$ is "flattened," while that in $CoCl_4^-$ is more regular.

8 Comment on the following statement, explaining why you think it right or wrong: "The neutral molecule $Ti(H_2O)_6$, in which the oxygen of each water molecule donates to Ti a lone pair, would be an unstable system with four electrons in the lower-energy d orbitals, but when all electrons except one are removed, the stable ion $Ti(H_2O)_6^{3+}$ results."

9 Calculate in electron volts the relative crystal field stabilization energy attained by the Fe^{++} ion in octahedral and tetrahedral oxide-ion environments.

10 Explain why the spinels $NiCr_2O_4$ and $CoFe_2O_4$ are normal and inverted, respectively.

11 If there were no crystal field effects, one would expect the ionic radii of doubly positive transition-metal ions to decrease slowly but gradually across the periodic table. Why? Actually a "curve" like the one shown in Fig. 6-14 is observed. Attempt an explanation, assuming a perfect octahedral weak field of oxide ions around the metal ion.

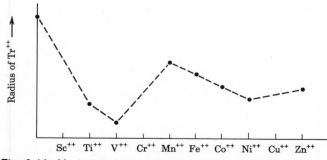

Fig. 6-14 Variation in metal-oxygen distances in oxides.

REFERENCES

1 L. E. Orgel, "An Introduction to Transition Metal Chemistry: Ligand Field Theory," Methuen & Co., Ltd., London, 1960.

2 D. Halliday and R. Resnick, "Physics for Students of Science and Engineering," 2d ed., part II, chap. 37: Magnetic Properties of Matter, John Wiley & Sons, Inc., New York, 1962.

3 F. Bitter, "Magnets: The Education of a Physicist," Doubleday Anchor Books, Garden City, N.Y., 1959.

4 R. G. Pearson, Crystal Field Explains Inorganic Behavior, *Chem. Eng. News,* **29,** 72 (1959).

5 L. Sutton, Some Recent Developments in the Theory of Bonding in Complex Compounds of the Transition Metals, *J. Chem. Educ.,* **37,** 498 (1960).

6 D. O'Reilly, Electronic Structure of Metal Oxides, *J. Chem. Educ.,* **38,** 312 (1961).

APPENDIX A:
UNITS OF ENERGY AND
CONVERSION FACTORS

At least four measures of energy are common in chemistry: the calorie, the erg, the electron volt, and the "wave number."

A calorie is roughly the amount of heat energy necessary to raise the temperature of one gram of water by one degree centigrade. One kilocalorie is one thousand calories.

The erg is the cgs unit of energy, and its relation to other cgs units can be easily remembered by noting the dimensions of kinetic energy, $\frac{1}{2}mv^2$. One erg is one g-cm^2/sec^2.

The electron volt (ev) is the kinetic energy an electron gains when accelerated through a potential difference of one volt in an electric field, and is a useful unit for researchers in electronic structure.

Spectroscopists find the unit "wave number" (cm^{-1}) very convenient, because it is simply the reciprocal of the photon wavelength expressed in centimeters. In Chap. 1 we learned that photon energy was inversely proportional to its wavelength ($E = hc/\lambda$), so that increasing $1/\lambda$ means increasing energy. Some authors have suggested the name kilokayser (kK) for the unit 1,000 cm^{-1}.

Some useful equalities relating these different energy units are

$$1 \text{ ev} = 1.602 \times 10^{-12} \text{ erg}$$
$$1 \text{ cal} = 4.184 \times 10^7 \text{ ergs} \qquad \text{(A-1)}$$
$$1 \text{ ev} = 8,065.7 \text{ cm}^{-1}$$

143

Frequently chemists discuss the energy associated with a process in terms of a mole of substance undergoing the change, i.e., in terms of kilocalories per mole rather than just kilocalories. Using the conversion equations (A-1) and Avogadro's number from Appendix B, prove for yourself that an energy of one electron volt is equivalent to an energy of 23.06 kcal/mole, i.e., that

1 ev = 23.06 kcal/mole   (A-2)

APPENDIX B:
VALUES OF
SOME PHYSICAL CONSTANTS

Speed of light	c	2.9979×10^{10} cm/sec
Planck's constant	h	6.6256×10^{-27} erg-sec
Electron charge	e	1.6012×10^{-19} coulomb (4.803×10^{-10} esu)
Mass of electron at rest	m	9.1091×10^{-28} g
Avogadro's number	N	6.0225×10^{23}

APPENDIX C: PERIODIC TABLE

PERIODIC TABLE OF THE ELEMENTS

Period	Ia	IIa	IIIa	IVa	Va	VIa	VIIa	VIII			Ib	IIb	IIIb	IVb	Vb	VIb	VIIb	0
1	1 H																1 H	2 He
2	3 Li	4 Be											5 B	6 C	7 N	8 O	9 F	10 Ne
3	11 Na	12 Mg											13 Al	14 Si	15 P	16 S	17 Cl	18 Ar
4	19 K	20 Ca	21 Sc	22 Ti	23 V	24 Cr	25 Mn	26 Fe	27 Co	28 Ni	29 Cu	30 Zn	31 Ga	32 Ge	33 As	34 Se	35 Br	36 Kr
5	37 Rb	38 Sr	39 Y	40 Zr	41 Nb	42 Mo	43 Tc	44 Ru	45 Rh	46 Pd	47 Ag	48 Cd	49 In	50 Sn	51 Sb	52 Te	53 I	54 Xe
6	55 Cs	56 Ba	57* La	72 Hf	73 Ta	74 W	75 Re	76 Os	77 Ir	78 Pt	79 Au	80 Hg	81 Tl	82 Pb	83 Bi	84 Po	85 At	86 Rn
7	87 Fr	88 Ra	89** Ac															

Transition series

*Lanthanide series	58 Ce	59 Pr	60 Nd	61 Pm	62 Sm	63 Eu	64 Gd	65 Tb	66 Dy	67 Ho	68 Er	69 Tm	70 Yb	71 Lu
**Actinide series	90 Th	91 Pa	92 U	93 Np	94 Pu	95 Am	96 Cm	97 Bk	98 Cf	99 Es	100 Fm	101 Md	102 No	103 Lw

APPENDIX D:
ANSWERS OR HINTS
FOR SOLUTION OF
SELECTED EXERCISES

Chap. 1

1 Radio waves, 2.8×10^{-9} kcal/mole; X-rays, 1.9×10^5 kcal/mole

2 1.8 to 3.0 ev

3 3×10^{-34} cm

4 1.2 Å

5 1.4×10^{-29} g

Chap. 2

2 (a) 13.6 ev

  (b) 218 ev

  (c) 163 ev

Chap. 3

1 2d and 3f are not possible within the rules stated in Sec. 3-2.

2 18, 2, 14, 50

6 *Hint:* Consider the increase in nuclear charge and also the effect of Hund's rule.

Chap. 4

1 *Hint:* Compare these molecules with smaller molecules of their families.

2 sp-hybridized carbon atoms; one σ and two π bonds with a circular cross section, as in the nitrogen molecule (Sec. 4-3).

3 HCl, 16.8 percent; HBr, 11.5 percent; HI, 4.9 percent

6 *Hint:* Approach the problem through the electron-pairing method.

7 *Hint:* The two structures made up of equivalent phosphorus atoms are a square and a perfect tetrahedron. The latter is experimentally established.

8 OF^+ with 16 electrons has two electrons unpaired in the antibonding π MO and is thus paramagnetic. Its bond order is 2, and it has the shortest bond distance and largest dissociation energy of the three. OF^- with 18 electrons is not paramagnetic. Its bond order is 1; its bond distance is the longest and its dissociation energy the smallest.

11 *Hint:* Note that borazole is isoelectronic with benzene, and also that boron is less electron-greedy than nitrogen.

Chap. 5

1 $E_{ic} = 5.82E_{ip}$, $U_{ic} = 1.46NE_{ip} = 171$ kcal/mole

2 With the assumption that $d = 2.05$ Å (the sum of the ionic radii) the stabilization energy with respect to the gaseous atoms is 442 kcal/mole.

3 Note that E_{rep} is equivalent to U_L/n, or 23 kcal/mole. The corrected lattice energy is thus 183 kcal/mole.

4 On the basis of ionic potential: most ionic, $BiCl_3$; least ionic, $BeCl_2$.

10 Decreasing hydrogen bonding: CH_3OH, CH_3NH_2, CH_3F, CH_4.

12 A is unlikely because of the small size of the proton; B is quite likely.

Chap. 6

3 *Hint:* Consider the linear field splitting diagram of Fig. 6-8c.

4 For square planar symmetry $\mu = 0$; for tetrahedral symmetry $\mu = 2.83$ BM.

5 d^3 in strong or weak fields, d^6 in strong fields, d^5 in weak fields, d^8 in strong or weak fields.

6 For d^1, larger; for d^2, smaller; for d^3, no preference on the basis of Jahn-Teller theorem.

7 *Hint:* Consider Jahn-Teller distortion.

9 From the spectrochemical series $\Delta(H_2O)$ is approximately equal to $\Delta(O^=)$. The octahedral Δ for Fe^{++} is 1.29 ev, and consequently for weak fields the octahedral *CFSE* is $\frac{2}{5}\Delta$, or 0.52 ev. The tetrahedral Δ is $\frac{4}{9}$ the octahedral Δ, or 0.57 ev, and consequently the tetrahedral *CFSE* is $\frac{3}{5}$ of this, or 0.34 ev.

11 *Hint:* Consider the shielding of the ligands from the metal nucleus by electrons in d_{xy}, d_{xz}, and d_{yz} orbitals relative to shielding by electrons in $d_{x^2-y^2}$ and d_{z^2} orbitals.

INDEX